GARY PLAYER
on fitness and success

GARY PLAYER
on fitness and success

GARY PLAYER with NORMAN HARRIS
PHOTOGRAPHS by GERRY CRANHAM

World's Work Ltd
Published in conjunction with The Sunday Times

SERIES EDITED BY JOHN LOVESEY
Sports Editor, The Sunday Times

Jogging
for fitness and pleasure
Cliff Temple

Swimming
a lifelong activity
John Lovesey

Everywoman
her guide to fitness
Chris Oram

Going Well Over 60
the road to fitness
Chris Oram

Fitness Afloat
rowing, sculling and canoeing
Richard Burnell

Badminton
playing for life
Richard Eaton

Orienteering
for fitness and pleasure
Norman Harris

Cycling
fitness on wheels
John Wilcockson

Fitness on Foot
climbing and walking for pleasure
Peter Gillman

Squash
a joyful game
John Hopkins

Text copyright © by Gary Player with Norman Harris 1979
Photographic copyright © by Gerry Cranham 1979

Published in Great Britain by World's Work Ltd
The Windmill Press, Kingswood, Tadworth, Surrey
In conjunction with *The Sunday Times*

Printed in Great Britain by
Morrison & Gibb Ltd, London and Edinburgh
SBN 437 12751 6

Contents

CHAPTER 1

Lessons of Golf and Life

My life revolves to a large extent around golf, and certainly it has earned me a good living; it is to my definite advantage, as a professional, that I am regarded as a famous golfer. However, I get most satisfaction from being, very simply, a fit person. When I wake up each morning my mood is not governed by the fact that I may have had a good round the day before and may win the tournament; it's governed by the fact that I feel well and it feels like a nice day. It may be an old cliché, but the day is what you make it. And I always do double my best to make it a good day.

I've always maintained that each morning you have the choice to be happy or be sad, and my belief that I do myself a favour by choosing the first way is reinforced by the people I see choosing sad.

This attitude, which some people may view as simplistic, has had its foundation in golf. When you are preparing for a putt, perhaps on the last green, perhaps with thousands of dollars hanging on it, you know that there are only two possibilities. Either you are going to make the putt or you are going to miss it. You know that from a certain distance you are going to make more putts than you are going to miss—if you have practised and prepared. So if I am putting on the 17th or 18th green to stay in a match I am only thinking of making it. Because I must make it, otherwise I'll be gone. It really is as simple as that.

Simplistic? When it boils down to it, most people's lives—each day—come down to alternatives like this. Do you worry yourself sick, when you can do nothing about the problem? Do you see the job through or do you not? Do you give the marriage a proper try or do you not?

All sport, but especially golf, teaches you that your fortunes are in your own hands. In golf you hit a stationary ball, and no one else can help or influence you. It's all down to you. So it is outside of sport. You are the head keeper, so to speak, of your own body. You have the keys. Your health prospects are much more in your own hands than in the hands of doctors and hospitals.

As I say, I am acutely aware of this, as a professional golfer. Every stroke I play on the course, every birdie and every bogie, every placing and every cheque, is a direct result of my physical and mental preparation: a direct result of my fitness. And if this is the case in a professional sport, why should it be any less so for a person in any other profession? When concentration/judgment/temper become frayed the potential consequence may be just as costly. To neglect one's own health and fitness is criminal.

When I started professional golf I was, of course, just a young man aiming to be fit enough to perform well on the golf course; I was healthy and I did not have to worry or even think much about these things. But gradually, especially as I realised I was approaching middle-age, I began to realise that there were much more important arguments for exercise and for a low-fat diet.

I learned about the arguments for giving exercise to the heart and lungs *for their own sakes*, so as to provide a greater tolerance to stress and generally improve the value of life, if not extend life itself. It made perfect sense. I learnt about fitness schemes in different countries, which were aimed at the whole population, especially at large work places. The merit of providing sporting facilities around factories seemed obvious, both to relieve boredom and also to improve fitness.

Typical of many such studies is one involving workers at a large company in Sweden, where those who did *not* take regular exercise were off sick and in hospital about three times more often than those who did take exercise. Even without such figures it makes sense that you can put in more hours if you're fit, and that this must be a benefit to the country, as well as to yourself and your family.

The idea is now catching on, but the main beneficiaries are mainly to be found in the middle-aged population. Corrective measures are fine (though in some cases sadly too late) but how much better to influence young people. I would like to see health made the compulsory first subject every day in schools. Surely it's a far more important topic to each individual, in the end analysis, than arithmetic, algebra or Latin.

We should teach children what happens when you smoke, and when

2

you drink. We should teach them about diet. We should encourage them to look closely at themselves, to understand what is good for them, what is bad for them, what upsets them, what makes them calm. I'm talking about mental as well as physical health. We wait until we are in our middle-age and desperate to escape the stresses of modern living, and then we buy books about yoga and jogging and diet and so on. Let's sow the seed much earlier.

In an ideal state I would also like to see couples who are about to be married receiving tuition in diet—not in the sense of laying down the law, but merely of discussing fat, protein, calories, vitamins. I say, "in an ideal state", yet are these objectives so radical or unrealistic?

Now a word about golf as an exercise sport. The fact is you probably won't see it in a very high position in any table of sporting activities graded according to their long-term fitness values. But it must also be apparent that I am a fit man, and so are other leading golfers. I have run to help achieve this, and other notable joggers are Graham Marsh and Lee Trevino. Jack Nicklaus was not prepared to handicap himself with the heavy poundage he carried around at the start of his career; his weight loss, and subsequent success, speak volumes for fitness and discipline.

Probably the greatest of all the "Fitness Golfers" is the legendary Sam Snead. Starting first thing in the morning, he works at his fitness every day. He keeps in magnificent shape. In fact I always describe him as the man with the rubber body. There is no question that he is the fittest and most successful 67-year-old golfer in the world.

What I am saying is that you have to be fit to play golf well. In fact you need to have a moderate level of fitness to play it at all. Most courses are about four miles long, and when they also contain a few hills you'll see men staggering up on to the green, so out of breath that they can't concentrate on putting the ball.

Mr. Executive, think of this: if you're not fit enough to get around the golf course, if you can't climb up on to the green and concentrate on the shot, how can you be fit enough to do a day's work in the office, to concentrate, move about and travel and make decisions?

Golf is an important exercise sport because it can increase fitness gradually from a very low starting level. It can build a platform, at least

3

of muscular capability, to which other activities can be added. And like other sports, it can play a most crucial role in creating an awareness of fitness.

When people get a taste for a sport they very rarely wish to just keep staggering along, as it were, at the same low level of fitness. They wish to enjoy the sport more by getting fitter. In this case they can do so by playing golf more often, or by adding other exercises (see Advanced Fitness, page 59).

Of course, you don't need to be as fit as a top tennis player or athlete. The gap between the average person who is fit and the top athlete is really nothing in terms of their long-term health status.

We must also take account of the fact that in this sport of golf the spectators can take as much exercise as the players they are watching. *That* can't be true of many sports. But if we are to look at golf mainly as a good game, which also provides some exercise, the best argument I can make for it is that people of different ability can play together and have a compelling competition because of the handicap system.

By contrast, take tennis. Even though I am proficient at tennis, if I played Bjorn Borg and he gave me a 40–0 start every game I'd still never win a game. No matter how many points he gave me, we still wouldn't have a contest to give either of us any satisfaction. But we could play golf quite satisfactorily even if he was a 24-handicapper. So can husbands and wives, and parents and youngsters.

My only regret is that golf does not have an image of sport-for-all, and does not pursue it. But it can be—it should be—a leading participation and exercise sport. To me it is the greatest sport in the world.

The final point I would like to make here concerns the balance of youth and age. The young man has energy and strength, but he is envious of the experience of the man of 50; the man of 50 envies the young man his energy and fitness. But what a man can do, as he acquires more experience and gets older, is to make it count over a longer period. And it must be true to say that the older man has a much better chance of holding on to his strength than the young man has of acquiring self-discipline, maturity and experience.

It is, if you like, *easier* for the older man—if he can view the matter in this positive way. Again, of course, golf is only reflecting life itself.

CHAPTER 2

An Early Diet
of No Excuses

There is a Chinese proverb which says that you have got to have determination to succeed in life, and you have got to suffer in the process. This rings very true to me. Especially in sport, and especially at the highest levels, I believe that the ability to accept adversity is of paramount importance.

I don't know of any sporting champions who grew up in an environment of wealth and comfort. I know I certainly didn't. It is true that we lived on a gold mine! But then, so did many other people in the Johannesburg suburb of Booysens. A large number of them worked in the mine, called Robinson Deep, and so did my father.

Harry Player had left school when his own father died at an early age, in order to support the rest of the family. Later, he made up some lost ground by studying hard for an examination which elevated him to Mine Captain status. But just around the corner there was a great shock for all of us. My mother died of cancer when she was 44.

I was then eight, and I have thought about it every time one of my own children has reached this age.

Going to school, on the other side of Johannesburg, meant getting up at 6 o'clock. It entailed a tram journey into the middle of the city, a walk for three-quarters of a mile, and then a bus out of town to King Edward VII school. The journey took me an hour and a quarter, twice a day, and it meant a good deal of walking. This I did from the age of seven.

I can remember taking off my shoes as soon as I got home, and scrupulously folding away my school clothes; they had to last because there was no money to replace them. And I can vividly remember the thrill of being taken into a store to buy a pair of tennis shoes which cost two shillings and six pence.

One of my father's main objections to making excuses was, simply, that no one wanted to hear them. This was also my mother's attitude in

5

the closing weeks of her life. It distressed my sister Wilma that mother would tell inquirers that she was "just fine" or "a little better today" when it was just not true. Mother's answer to Wilma was that people have their own troubles and don't want to hear anyone else complain. There is probably something of the pioneer attitude in this, and in fact we don't have to go very far back in our South African history to find the roots. My great-grandmother, of French Hugenot descent, was a child in the Great Trek of the 1830s, and survived a Zulu massacre by dragging herself off into the bush with a spear in her side.

My brother Ian has a lot of that sort of determination, as well as the dislike of excuses. His right knee was badly smashed in a climbing accident when he was 12 and was always to give him trouble; but he never gave in to it or complained. It caused him to be rejected when, at just 16, he tried to enlist in the army for the war in Europe. He kept on trying until finally he was accepted, and he served in a tank brigade in Italy.

I can remember that the early evenings were a lonely time, as I waited for my father and sister to come home from work. But I cannot remember ever feeling sorry for myself. I think that is because father had made it clear that difficulties or hardships must be seen as challenges and must be answered positively. He was a man who on one hand would brook no excuses, and could be quite brusque in dismissing them, and on the other hand was a very affectionate and loving father. I don't think that in fact there is any contradiction or inconsistency here. I have a lot of my father in me, and indeed I used gladly to kiss him good morning and good night right through to the end of his life.

I'm happy to see myself as someone who is sentimental and easily hurt, yet ready to accept discipline and hard work. I can do no better than offer the example of one of my great heroes, Winston Churchill. I understand that he cried very easily, though he was a tiger on the battlefield.

I was very fortunate that my parents made the effort to send me all the way to King Edward's school. It's motto was an inspiration in itself: *Strenue*—With All Our Might. Indeed, the school has produced leaders throughout the business and professional world, and a host of sporting champions. Almost 80 King Edward boys have represented

their country at a major sport, and 14 have been cricketing Springboks—
including one of the most recent South African captains, Dr. Ali Bacher.
For me, golf was to be some way off as I tackled soccer, rugby,
cricket, athletics and swimming. But the sports in which I won double
colours, a rare honour, were cricket and rugby.

Strangely enough, in a rugby-mad country, I had started by playing
soccer in the preparatory school and when eventually at the age of 13,
I found myself in a rugby game, I had very little idea of what was required of me. I asked a friend what to do. He said: "Look, you play on
the wing, and when you get the ball you just run for that line. And if
you get over the line with the ball, you will be in the team." The first
time I had the ball I did as told. I charged through. There was no one
that was going to stop me. Eventually I played scrum half for the school,
and then fly half.

One of the school magazines made the following comment on this
particular member of the 1st XV: "He is an artful dodger . . . slow off
the mark but seems to respect monkeys and emulates their tactics."

They got away with such remarks by putting them in a column en-
titled Non-Malicious Comments! But I do feel, in my heart of hearts,
that if I had pursued rugby I could have been a Springbok scrum half.
I had the determination and I wasn't scared of anything, including
being thumped.

As a cricketer, I performed mainly as an off-spin bowler. On one
fortuitous occasion, this brought seven wickets for one run, including
two hat-tricks. In athletics I competed in the hurdles and as a swimmer
I concentrated mainly on diving, so I suppose I must have had the
advantage of a certain amount of natural athleticism. And, of course,
I was sport mad.

How I was regarded, apart from being the school's No. 1 sportsman,
is a good question. I would guess I might be remembered as a fellow
who tried really hard in his sports, and less so in his schoolwork; and
a fellow who was very concerned about being popular. Whether this last
aspect came across to others I'm not sure, but I was certainly very
concerned to be liked. I also got very upset when other boys were derided
for being Afrikaners or Jews.

Of course, we never see ourselves as others see us. So to get a clearer

7

picture of these interesting years, some recollections were invited from others who were at King Edward's at that time. One was a master—a Scot, Mr. Derby Whyte, with whom I have always kept in close touch. In fact, he has visited me on the overseas circuit.

At the British Open he was rather struck by the way we professionals pulled each other's legs relentlessly and made comments which an outsider would consider ludicrous. He decided to play the same game.

When he was introduced to Arnold Palmer as my old school sports master, Arnold asked him: "Say Mr. Whyte, I've heard so much of this wonderful school of Gary's—what sort of kid was he at school?"

Derby Whyte replied gravely: "Man, Arnie, I have to confess that he was one of our failures."

Arnie was temporarily thunderstruck. "A failure? Well please keep your successes out of my hair. He is the only guy in the world who comes to the States and regularly pinches the cream of our coffee."

Derby Whyte provided a detailed, candid and, I hope, interesting document about those schooldays. First he discusses an extraordinary cricket match which I had almost forgotten, and then goes on to other matters:

"One of the most remarkable cricket matches in the annals of King Edward VII school took place on February 13th, 1952, at home to St. John's College. The visitors batted first and declared their innings closed at 221 for nine wickets. King Edward's then started so disastrously that within a very short time their score stood at 32 for six. There was an improvement after that to 125 for seven. Gary Player and R. A. Hoffman—the captain who had opened the innings—came together when two more wickets had fallen and the score stood at 144 for nine. In other words, last man was in and they were 67 runs short. It looked utterly hopeless but Player and Hoffman refused to give in. St. John's tried every wile known to cricketers to get them to put up a catch, but there they stayed. Finally with boys, masters, parents and Bantu groundsmen screaming in unison every time a run was made, they hit the winning single and the score stood at 222 for nine.

"Gary Player was a most unusually serious-minded child and, although he loved fun and games as much as any other boy of that age, he was very outspoken and meant every word he said. Everybody who

An Early Diet of No Excuses

knows him must have remarked the straight-looking, candid brown eyes and the strongly-arched dark eyebrows that gave an unusual intensity to his spoken thoughts. This forthright trait did not always endear him to his elders or even to schoolboys senior to himself—but he has always been, to my knowledge, immaculately polite.

"Most schools arrange their games and athletics programmes in age groups, and this can mean a serious drawback to young, and especially small, boys. A child born at the end of the year must compete with his fellow born in, say, January. Player's birthday is in November, so he did have a disadvantage in competition. He learned early on the qualities he had to acquire in order to survive and win. As a school sports master I have often observed this phenomenon and it has urged me to the conclusion that the spiritual attributes are much more important than the physical in the development of the human ego and determination to succeed."

A schoolmate, Frank Hodgkinson, has provided an even more personal note on the subject of our competitions! My friend Frank recalls:

"From the very first, Gary's determination to win, and his ability to concentrate and his belief in himself were evident. He was particularly determined in sporting events and in personal forms of competition. He was very keen on weightlifting and very proud of his feats at push-arm. If you should ever happen to beat him he would train for weeks and you would get no peace until he had finally, in turn, beaten you."

It is certainly true that from an early age I was involved in exercises and strength tests outside of school sports. We had a makeshift weight-lifting "set" with the weights provided with the wheels from one of the trolley cars which trundle sand and stone out of the mines. I can also remember boxing, and belting away at a punch bag.

In all this my elder brother Ian was a tremendous driving force. From an old pear tree in the garden he tied a rope to the highest branch, about 30 feet up. He told me if I wanted to be able to look after myself I should climb that rope every day. The daily routine certainly built up my arms and shoulders, and with the strength came self-confidence. Eventually I was climbing up using only hands—no feet—and I can still do that today.

9

An Early Diet of No Excuses

Ian was also keen on running for fitness. He had a regular course from our house, and he persevered with this even though handicapped with his knee. One day he took me on a mile run. Even though I was barely 10, he seemed to make no allowances and kept pressing me on. Finally, about halfway through, I gave up. I said, "I can't run any more." At this he became very angry. He gave me one hell of a kick in the rear and said, "Don't let me ever hear you say *can't*." I didn't thank him for it at the time, but I completed that one-mile run.

If Ian may seem from that story a harsh taskmaster he also provided challenge and encouragement. He knew that I had something of a complex about being small. Sometimes I would be called "shorty" by other boys, and once when it was said to me on a school athletics afternoon, I promptly won the 100 yards, the 220 yards, the 440 yards and the 880 yards, and then confided to Ian my feelings that this was not a bad effort for "a shorty".

When we were doing other exercises, like push-ups, and I had reached my limit, he would offer me a prize if I did another 10. I would then win the prize—or bribe—and he would say, "Just a minute ago you said you couldn't do it."

But what I mainly remember is that run, and the kick, and the way Ian scorned the word *can't*. His words formed the basis of a motto. This motto may not actually be on the wall, or on my desk, but it doesn't have to be. I can visualise it, all the time. The word CAN'T has the T crossed out so that it becomes CAN.

CHAPTER 3

The Lonely Challenge

If my brother Ian seemed a hard taskmaster, he was, like my father, motivated by concern and idealism. He has since gained world-wide renown as an expert on ecology and the preservation of wildlife. And, although he kicked me for stopping on that run, he also whittled my first golf club from a stick.

My father, however, was the main golfer in the family. Mine company workers could play at the local club, which was situated above the mine, for a small subscription. On Saturday afternoons and Sundays he worked hard at his game. A big man, though without great natural ability, he did very well to bring his handicap down to 2.

I was almost 15 when one day he suggested that I come and play golf with him. My instant reaction was to say no. Golf was a game for cissies and I really wasn't interested. But the second time he asked me I went along. And I had three pars on each of the first three holes.

Now this really was quite extraordinary. It was the first time I had hit golf balls on a golf course. Previous to this I had swung my father's clubs around a bit, though he was a left-hander. There was also some swinging of the wire clubs made by caddies—thick steel wire bent into an appropriate shape, to hit a rubber ball. And, going back further, a game we played as children called Kenneky; this involved wielding a wooden club, scraping a smaller piece of wood out of a trough in the ground, and clouting it as it spun up into the air. I suppose the various school sports must also have developed my co-ordination. Even so, this hardly explains three straight pars.

The first was a par 3, hitting across water. The next was a short downhill 4. The third was a fairly tough 4 with out-of-bounds on the right and a little river coming across the approach to the green.

I can only conclude that I didn't know what the hell I was doing. I didn't know enough to be scared. I was totally relaxed.

They call it beginner's luck, but it isn't just luck, and there is certainly a lesson here about our approach to games. The fact is, I deteriorated fairly rapidly after those first three holes, and ended up with a score too high to want to remember.

Still, I had the golf bug. The sport had an irresistible challenge, because it was so difficult and demanding. I still played my team sports at school. But in golf I couldn't pass the ball and get rid of the problem. I was the only person involved and I was the only person who could make things happen. This was the beauty of golf.

I worked at it like fury. In the evenings I would putt and chip on the carpet, and do lots of club swinging on a big rubber mat. I'd get up early and practise in the park, driving golf balls through the rugby posts. I started playing at weekends.

Most important of all, I met Vivienne Verwey, whose father was the golf professional at Virginia Park Golf Course. We played golf together, and Mr. Verwey coached me in the basics of the golf swing. In fact he still gives me regular help on technique.

The first time I saw Vivienne I said to my stepbrother, Christopher: "Isn't that a lovely girl? I tell you what, I'm going to marry that girl one day." There may have been an element of chance in the fact that I said it, and it happened. But I always have tended to see the future directly.

Derby Whyte recalls that this attitude also caused amusement at King Edward's, when golf was discussed:

"The name of Bobby Locke came up. Probably it was a reference to his winning of the British Open again.

"Player observed in his solemn way, 'That is what I would like to be —a golf pro.'

"A boy in the class said teasingly, 'You mean just like Bobby Locke?'

" 'Of course that is what I mean,' replied Player, 'a world champion like Locke.' He accompanied this declaration with a characteristic punching movement of the right arm.

"This caused much merriment and more teasing.

"My own contribution to this small talk was to the effect that it was a fine thing to have big ambitions but to accomplish such an ambition as this would require a long, hard struggle to get to the top and an even harder struggle to stay there.

"With the advantage of hindsight it is quite remarkable how the small boy's wish, expressed some 30 years ago, has been fulfilled. It was so apparent to me that he meant what he said that it awakened an interest in the progress of the boy that has never since abated."

It's certainly true that at the time everyone I knew was distinctly unimpressed by the idea of my trying to make a career in professional golf. I was warned that the flagrant neglect of my duties would lead, without any doubt, to disaster.

My mathematics master told me that unless I got better grasp of this subject I wouldn't earn a brass farthing after I left school.

Another master told me, "If you don't stop this golf nonsense you will never get anywhere in life."

Understandably, Mr. and Mrs. Verwey were also concerned when I told them that I wanted to marry their daughter, and I intended to support her by becoming a champion golfer.

Even my father was sceptical. But, typically, he gave me his whole-hearted support when he realised that I was set on the idea. He ended up by giving me a new set of golf clubs—my first *new* set—with which to travel to Britain.

It was only some years afterwards that I learnt from our bank manager that an overdraft had been agreed in order to finance this purchase.

Looking back, I guess I had everything I needed. Ambition, determination, energy and new clubs!

CHAPTER 4

The Anatomy of Golfing Success

If you asked me, when I was starting out, what it takes to be one of the best golfers in the world, I'd probably have thought in terms of hitting the ball better than anyone else. Hitting it further from the tee, hitting it longer to the green. Now I realise differently.

Golf is too intricate, too demanding a game, to be able to say this. There are so many golfers who hit the ball well; and a good number who don't hit the ball so well, yet are still successful.

It's tempting to think that Bobby Locke was a great champion because of his putting, and Ben Hogan because of his driving. Well, these may have been the departments in which they excelled, but they were by no means the foundation on which the success was built.

Obviously natural ability is an important factor. I believe most top golfers have a degree of ball-playing ability, even if they don't always look like athletes. Several of today's top players, for example, are excellent tennis players, and Jack Nicklaus was also very good at basketball. Obviously I had some games-playing ability which gave me a good start. However, I was considered too small to "make it", and my golf swing wasn't all that good.

As for being small, I certainly don't think it's been any disadvantage. In fact it's a funny thing to be reminded that I am so short on inches. Every time I catch a sight of myself walking by a mirror it's a bit of a shock to realise that I'm a tiny little guy.

I see a picture of myself in the newspaper, on the course beside someone like Andy Bean. I look like an ant! And yet when I'm out there I feel like a giant! I feel I could tear anyone apart if I had to. It's just a *feeling*, of course. Something in the mind. But it's a wonderful feeling.

I suppose fitness is what we're really talking about here. Because there are many facets to fitness, and you become aware of them as you get older.

In the first place it's the strength which you build into yourself—the sort of strength I realised that I was missing, despite all the exercising I'd done since boyhood, when I first went to America in 1956 and played the Masters.

I couldn't get over how short I was playing on the long par-5 holes. And the other fellows were knocking over these par 5s. I said to myself, "If you ever want to win this tournament you've got to improve the strength in your hands and arms and legs." I did eventually make a big improvement in my length off the tee—through weightlifting and by stretching the length of my swing.

In the second place it is the ability to hang on to that strength, to sustain effort as you get older. I think this is proven by my having won the Masters—for the third time—at the age of 42; and I can certainly say that I feel as strong on a golf course these days as I did when I was 20.

The third facet of fitness, and it's one which is extremely subtle and hard to define, is that it makes you *aware* of your physical condition. It makes you appreciate vital good health.

When I am asked what it feels like to hit a full-blooded drive I have to say that the best way to describe it is in terms of a spring. It's like a cat springing. Of course, the result of the drive doesn't *always* match this image! But at least it's better to have this feeling on the tee than to be just praying that you stay out of trouble.

Now we come to another highly important part in sporting success, and one that's even harder to define. Every now and again I get into discussion about this with golfers and other sportsmen, and I call this factor Energy.

It's very far from a matter just of how much sugar you've got in your system, available to be utilised as fuel for the muscles, because I believe energy is also very much to do with desire, with ambition, with application and determination, and with personality. These are unfathomed depths for the medical profession, but we sportsmen recognise the factor when we see it.

I get my leg pulled about whether I use batteries, or get wound up, or have some other supplementary power source. There have been many sporting champions with the same sort of generator, including some rather unlikely ones.

The Anatomy of Golfing Success

The obvious one from the world of athletics is Emil Zatopek, who used to train about twice as hard as anyone else *and* enjoy it—even when he used to practise holding his breath until he blacked out!

An even more interesting example is someone like Britain's champion of 40 years ago, Sydney Wooderson. A solicitor, he lived a very well-ordered life, enjoying his office work and also his suburban home-life. He was retiring by nature. But there was *"that something"*, as he said, which made him run like a bat out of hell.

I have to admit, I'm not so retiring by nature! But I still put my energies down to the same sort of thing. Something in the blood that can't be analysed. I often say it's a case of having the "genes".

Having said that, let's look at the other side of the coin. You can't drive a car at top speed if the tyres are half flat, and it is obvious that I have been able to drive myself through the last 25 years only because the mechanics have been in top order. And it is equally obvious to me that if I let my physical condition deteriorate, that "energy" would soon run out and those "genes" would count for nothing.

We've looked at Talent and, in its various forms, Fitness. Now comes the Mind. The old brain-box. It can make us, and it can beat us, and there are many times when it is the *only* factor which holds the balance. On one side you have the fear element pressing in at you, and on the other side you've got the positive thoughts.

I see it in terms of the Steamroller and the Mouse. You've got to make the positive thoughts the steamroller and fearful thoughts the mouse. Unfortunately it is often the other way around, and the negative thoughts turn into the steamroller.

The human being, for all the fact that he is an amazing machine, can also be very, very weak. He can feel very pessimistic and very sorry for himself. That is why I appreciate the doctrine that my father and brother hammered into me: No Excuses!

I am now trying to impress it on my son Wayne, who is planning to be a professional golfer. He has to try and make the grade despite the fact that he hasn't had to accept adversity. I don't wish hardship on him, though. But I can try and help him as my father helped me. I try to tell him that I'm not interested in how well he hit the ball but what he scored.

The Anatomy of Golfing Success

When he played in Britain for the first time, in 1978, he often found the conditions unpleasant compared with the year-round sunshine of South Africa. He bemoaned the fact that there was wind and rain, and the cold which caused him to wear two sweaters.

At this, I would say to him: "Tell me, son, when all the other fellows were on the course they were playing in sunshine, right? And you were in the rain? It was only blowing on the hole you were playing?"

I told him to think how bad other people must be feeling, and to get in there and make the best of the opportunity. It is only really a matter of thinking positively instead of negatively.

I am really talking about all of life—for there are many different things we have to practise from time to time—but one of the best examples I can give comes, again, from the world of sport.

In athletics a well-known tactic is for essentially strong runners to use surges of speed, or "burners", to shake off opponents who will have superior speed if they're still around at the finish. If the tactic is going to work it will surely need a succession of "burners"—as many as have been planned—for the scheme to work. The chap will have to follow his plan through and he will probably have to suffer in the process. It is no good his abandoning the plan at an early point because it doesn't seem to be working. In fact this has been the failing of more than one world-class runner.

My inclination would be to try even harder when something isn't working. I tend to respond to the challenge of being down and almost written off. In fact some people would say that is what really produces the best of my golf.

There was a well-publicised incident during the famous match with Tony Lema in the Piccadilly of 1965, when I was 7-down and got angry when I overheard a spectator remark that I had no chance.

In fact there was another remark, a private one, which also produced a reaction at that time—and I take no great pride in recalling it. Vivienne came across to me and tried to say something encouraging: she said she loved me. I snapped back at her that I did not need sympathy on the golf course; all I wanted to do was fight and fight.

Afterwards I felt very badly about this. I knew how Vivienne was suffering for me. My only consolation was that she also had the understanding to accept that my outburst was a reflection only of the golf situation and my determination not to give up in this battle.

The more I play golf, the more I'm inclined to think that the mental factors have the greatest bearing on success. It goes almost without saying that the most successful golfers are characterised by even temperaments. Today, Jack Nicklaus is a Champion of the Even Disposition; probably no golfer has ever been so successful in accepting mishaps on the course, placing them behind him, and still managing to return a good score.

And of course, one of the best examples was given to me from the start—by Bobby Locke. Here was a man whose every action was slow and deliberate, almost as if this was a *mechanism* which was ensuring that he was never flustered.

There is a great story told of how in a Wentworth tournament Locke started with a 7 on a par-5 and a 5 on a par-3, and played on (eventually emerging with a sterling 74) and did not refer to it until at the 13th hole he said to his playing partner: "You know, that was a pretty silly thing I did on the first two holes."

Now this is wonderful patience and control—and for me, with my enthusiasm and impatience, this is a particularly hard battle to have to win.

Recently an idea has been advanced that sport is entirely an Inner Game, and a book by this title uses tennis to illustrate the argument. Basically the argument is that it's not your opponent who beats you but yourself. The key to success is being able to switch off from the contest. If you enjoy your *own play*, with such a complete and almost hypnotic involvement that you are scarcely aware of your opponent or the score, you are in fact much more likely to win as a consequence.

This argument does seem to be based on sound principles, though whether it has as much relevance for golf I don't know.

The fact is you don't really have an opponent in golf; you're already playing against yourself, to a large extent, and I believe that concentration and positive thoughts are the proper allies in striking the ball successfully. In other words, it is *control* which is important, rather than avoiding the normal controls.

Just think for a moment about what golf entails and what makes it,

19

I believe, the toughest of games. The ball is tiny and the playing surface is as large as 300 acres: that's a far higher ratio than in any other ball sport. And that vast playing area is always different—from one course to another, from one day to another on the same course, and from one hole to another on the same day. There are huge wind variables, wetness and dryness of grass, sand which is wet, dry and "fluffy", greens which are fast, slow, hard and soft. There are water hazards and out-of-bounds stakes and, most of all, the unpredictable bounce of the ball.

You can hit the better drive off the tee but your ball can end up with a bad lie, while the other fellow's is sitting up nicely. He may get a birdie 3 and you may get a 5.

In fact, you could say that accepting adversity—rather than hitting brilliant shots—is what golf is all about. If it is, it means that this sport has the most marvellous application to the rest of life. I often think of the sentiment expressed first by Sir Francis Bacon, and endorsed by Harry Truman: "The good things which belong to prosperity are to be wished for, but the good things that belong to adversity are to be admired."

On the golf course, you can accept adversity much more calmly if you're mentally well prepared. If you do badly at the first hole, that's almost part of the plan. You know that there's no such things as playing all the holes well, so you say: "All right, somewhere along the way I'm going to have a bad hole, and it's happened at the first hole. I'm feeling good and I'm going to do so well that it doesn't really matter."

I remember the British Open of '74, when I was leading by six strokes and went into a bunker, the first bunker shot left the ball in the sand and I took a 5 on a par-3; and the next hole I again went into a bunker, and instead of being affected by what had happened on the previous occasion, approached the shot just as positively as I normally would a bunker shot.

It doesn't *always* work like this. At the 1978 PGA tournament, I four-putted the very first hole of the tournament, and then let frustration get the upper hand. I felt sorry for myself and blamed the narrow fairways and fast greens, and the time change in having travelled from Britain. I felt negative, and played negatively.

So I have a clear picture in my own mind of what it's like to be on the top side and the down side of this mental slope. What we're talking about comes down to Concentration for most people, and because this is such an important subject in so many different sports, I propose to expand on it in a separate chapter.

CHAPTER 5

Concentrating the Mind

If I am asked whether there has been any one tournament which was definitely won because I had the right attitude of mind, I can say that without a shadow of coubt it was the US Open of 1965.

By some way, I put more into this tournament than any other. My motivation was that it was the only major Open I had never won; and all week previously I had been reading Dr. Vincent Peale's book *The Power of Positive Thinking*.

One of the mental strategies I put into practice was one in which you visualise what is going to happen. This can mean standing on the tee and concentrating on the line the ball will take and where it will finish on the fairway. At Bellerive in 1965 it also meant looking at the scoreboard, before the event, and visualising my name up there ate the end of the list of previous winners. Every time I walked past that board I saw my name.

I won the title, and I could almost say that I hypnotised myself into winning it.

In the days prior to the start of the championship I went around methodically checking out the transport, the locker rooms and every other thing or place that would involve me. I lived like a hermit. I deliberately moved very slowly. I talked slowly, dressed slowly. I was working myself into a sort of reverie.

I went to the Catholic church down the road. It was the nearest church to the motel, and in fact this was the first time I had attended a Catholic service. I wanted to go to a quiet place to get some peace of mind and I also wanted to pray. I prayed for courage, strength and patience, and I thanked God for all the good things in life, including adversity.

I see this as a building up of one's inner strength. People might say that you can only build up strength that you have. That's not correct. Why is it that one day you can't pick up a weight of, say, 120 pounds, and the next day—because for some reason you're so damn mad you've

23

got extra strength—you can throw up that 120 easily? This is where the human being is so fantastic.

As I've said previously, we human beings are very subject to the competing forces of positive and negative thoughts. The steamroller and the mouse was one image I used. Perhaps an even better one is the idea of two magnets opposing each other. The smaller magnet attracts the positive thoughts and the bigger one the negative thoughts; so what we've got to try to do is rest the negative one and make the positive one work overtime.

Let me tell you a story of a positive shot. It came about in the PGA tournament in 1972. There were several of us within one stroke and at the 16th I hit the ball into the rough on the right. To attack the green from there required a shot directly over a willow tree, and over water, and the pin was close to the water. I thought of playing safe and trying to retain my one-stroke lead; and I thought of letting rip at the flag. I decided that to win you have to play like a winner—*positively*—and I fired it at the flag. In fact it settled three feet from the pin.

As the crowd rushed forward, one man went to where the divot lay. He took it away and apparently planted it in his yard, with all due ceremony. He later claimed that quite a patch of grass grew from it. The man was evidently a golfer. He must have weighed up the situation and assumed I was going to play safe. The opposite choice, and the shot, impressed him enough to want to keep a memento of it. Every time he saw the lawn he thought of that shot and that positive act.

I have gone through periods in my golf career where I have been intent and relatively silent on the course, and then I've played with someone who has liked to chat. And I've thought, well maybe it *is* a good idea to relax. So I've chatted and joked. But of course this is foolish. I've let the other fellow take me to his level. I should have made him come to mine.

I'm not making judgment on the way other people play but take Lee Trevino. He loves to talk. It doesn't seem important whether he's talking to his partner, to someone in the crowd, or to his golf bag. He obviously gets rid of his tension by nattering and joking, and it is no more a fault in him than stern silence is in someone like Ben Hogan. But it can be unnerving if you let it be.

Working at exercise with Player

Gary Player. Age: 43. Height: 5ft 7 in. Weight: 150 lb. Medical tests have shown pulse rate, blood pressure, lung capacity and blood cholesterol to be all better than average—in some cases dramatically better. His weight is the same as it was when playing first-team rugby at the age of 16. He has to work at it, and does so gladly, believing that keeping one's weight down is one of the secrets of good health. "People musn't be scared of getting thin as they get older."

Once, as a young golf pro at a club, Player used to make a little extra money by walking on his hands around the edge of a billiards table. Now, the physical exploits play an important role in self-preservation. Note that the conventional press-up and the much tougher one-handed variety are performed without cutting any corners: in each case the horizontal plane is rigidly maintained, and the stomach and nose touch the ground together. And what the golfer's arms can do, so can the legs. The one-legged squat, with the body forced upright from this sitting position, argues exceptional strength in the thighs.

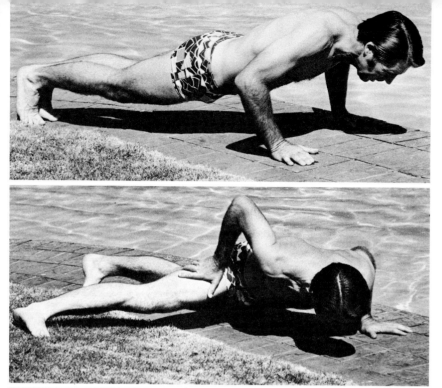

The knee pulled up hard underneath the chin is aimed specifically at flexing and strengthening the lower back. The "Rabbit Jumps", as he calls them, have a completely different purpose. It's not only the height of the jump that's important, it's the fact that there's a succession of them, (and he also turns as he jumps, so that he completes circles). Doing "sets" of these—as with most of the other exercises—means that the lungs and heart are being given a vigorous workout.

More strength exercises.
These are the ones Player
works at most, with the
weighted shoe and the heavy
golf club travelling with him
everywhere. The special club
has a thick shaft and a steel
head, and weighs 8 pounds
compared with the normal
13 ounces. Swinging it with
two hands is one thing,
swinging it with one hand
is another; and holding it
between two fingers, without
help from the thumb, is in fact
the most demanding exercise
on these pages. Less arduous,
and of great benefit to
lesser mortals, is running on
the spot. It is Player's main
recommendation for those
who are unfit and want to do
something about it. He
advocates running-on-the-
spot, swimming and
stretching exercises.

Swimming, especially the butterfly stroke, is another rigorous exerciser of the heart and lungs. As a runner, practising for a Superstars contest, Player was timed at $5\frac{1}{2}$ minutes for a mile on an athletics track—a fast time for a non-athlete, and indeed for only an occasional runner. When he gets to his farm he likes to go for a run and clear his lungs out in air which "contains not one speck of pollution". And when moving about the farm, he likes to jog instead of walk. It keeps him "ticking over". It gets the heart pumping.

At tennis, he rates his ability as "probably equivalent to a nine handicap at golf". But this is a game which serves another purpose: judicious selection of partners for a doubles game means that the family can have a well-balanced and enjoyable contest.

Concentrating the Mind

You mustn't fall into the trap. I now play *my* way all the time, which is pretty much a matter of isolating myself. A year after winning the 1978 Masters, for instance, my partner during the last round, Severiano Ballesteros, told me that he twice spoke to me during that round and I did not answer him. I wasn't aware of this.

In my book, concentration doesn't apply only during each round. It should be woven into each 24 hours of the tournament. Many golfers practise quite hard but most of them think that when their work in practise or competition is over, the day is done. That's why there are so few champions. Sure, there is a time for relaxation after each day's golf. But it shouldn't just be a matter of saying, "It's a new day tomorrow." The golfer should be analysing what he did and what he didn't do, what his intentions will be in the future rounds, visualising what he intends to happen. He should be, at the same time, relaxing and concentrating. Building up mind power.

With more success, we all develop more commitments off the course, which paradoxically works against more success. But I am quite sure in my own mind that *if* I put aside all these other activities and concentrated exclusively on golf for a year, then there's no knowing what success could follow.

I also believe that a young man could be *made* into a champion. This is theory, of course, and it is not feasible to carry it out. In my theoretic argument you would take a young all-round sportsman with good ball sense. He would have to know that his life depended on following your direction, and you would have complete control over his time. He would have to practise hard. He would have to take a lot of exercise. He would need to follow the best nutritional advice. And he would need to be guided in the art of positive mental attitude.

What this mental guidance would amount to is not quite my territory. I can only describe—as I have done—how I believe it works for me. To gain more insight into this fascinating area of concentration, I have talked at some length to a group of professionals in psychology, Dr. Richard Maddock, Dr. Charles T. Kenny and Dr. Ray Sexton, who have a good deal of professional and personal interest in this area. In their private practice in Memphis, Tennessee, they consult with athletes on all levels. The following, which comes from them, addresses itself mainly to the problem of concentration. I hope that it will be of interest to all sports people.

When athletes and others talk about concentration, they are usually focusing on the tremendous importance that the mind plays in the overall ability of the athlete to come to the top. Concentration is only part of the mental preparation that is so important for success in all sports, and is so crucial in golf.

All golfers have suffered poor form from day to day, a good swing breaking down, sudden slumps reflected in high scores, and have been puzzled by this. Our experience in this field is that such puzzles can frequently be explained by pointing to mental and psychological factors.

Psychologically, many individuals allow themselves to be *done in* by fear. Their personalities won't tolerate the bombardment. These golfers must conquer their personality limitations in prayer, meditation, psychotherapy, mental preparation, positive mental attitudes, experience, or whatever it takes before they can reach their true potential in golf.

A golfer who is prone to give way to these fears will lose concentration for varying lengths of time. In golf, as you know, this loss of concentration can be disastrous.

A further point is that the game of golf offers a very long 'pathway to success'—usually between 6,000 and 7,000 yards—with very many distractions. There's the scenery, the gallery, other golfers, conversation, hazards and entrapments.

At all times the tiny ball is carefully guarded by the player. There is an urgency to get the ball up in the air. With all of this pressure along with the distractions of keeping the eye on the ball and concentrating on the mechanics, concentration is easily reduced to a minimum.

There are few other sports (compare: basketball, soccer, tennis) that require an individual to be sociable while engaging in the sport. Since concentration is essential in every sport, and since there are so many hazards to concentration in golf, the area of mental preparation is therefore essential.

So let's talk about mental preparation. The mind is especially susceptible to *suggestions*. Those who work in advertising have known this for many years. It is necessary to get suggestions into the mind in order to bring about the desired effect upon people.

Concentrating the Mind

An advertiser markets a product by giving you a suggestion to buy, and the desired effect is to get you up and moving to the store to buy his product. Similarly, in athletics, the weightlifter not only lifts weights, but often does it in front of a mirror where he can observe the activities of his muscles and make continuous suggestions to himself about the improvement that he sees and feels.

Medicine and psychology are aware of the intricate interaction of the mind and the body. Coordination of muscles and muscle groups are directly controlled by complex nerve pathways in the brain. These pathways have complex input from emotional centres as well as input from chemical centres. These emotional centres are receptacles for suggestions. When the appropriate suggestions are placed into the mind the proper function of motor and muscle activity are greatly enhanced and the desired behaviour will result.

For example, in certain patients that we have worked with who have high blood pressure, selective mental work on their heart and blood pressure muscles will relieve tension, pressure and stress, in turn allowing them to lower their blood pressure. Similarly, they can change their heart rate, reduce pain, and increase circulation. On the other hand, if negative suggestions go into the mind, results will be negative.

To understand how suggestions affect performance, we like to think of three different sides of man. The first is man's behaviour, which anyone can observe. The second side of man is his thinking processes. Logical thinking and problem-solving are good examples of this. Thinking, as we use the term, refers to the conscious activity of the mind. The third side of man that we emphasise are his feelings.

By feelings we refer to emotions and even thoughts that are mostly outside the scope of awareness. In other words, we are speaking of the unconscious part of the mind.

Now all three parts of man interact with one another to form a feedback loop. Behaviour affects thinking, thinking in turn affects feelings. Thoughts control feelings and feelings control behaviour.

If the behaviour is good, it cycles back and creates good thoughts. Similarly, if the behaviour that results is bad, it cycles back and creates bad thoughts and the whole process or cycle is started over again.

When a golfer on a water hole plays a bad shot and finds the creek this can influence what he thinks of the next time he hits the ball, and especially the next time he finds a water hole.

He might think, 'I've got to stay out of the water' or 'I'll need a longer club.'

These uneasy feelings interfere with concentration and reduce confidence. The result is that they are likely to affect the behavioural level thereby helping to create a poor shot and closing the feedback loop once again.

A cycle like this can get started and create a trap or slump, so that the golfer gets trapped into the cycle of poor performance and can't get out. Some golfers have the type of personality which is more prone to this type of negative mental process than others, and shortly we will review some remedies for this.

Let's take an example of this vicious cycle. Imagine that the last time you played the ninth hole of your home course, your first shot went out of bounds and your second shot landed in the trap which resulted eventually in a triple bogey. You never recovered your previous momentum and had several miserable holes. You really felt uneasy about your game. Eventually you go back to work and other things occupy your mind, although your doubts about golf remain in a vague sort of a way in the back of your mind.

On the next trip back to play, all of those negative thoughts which were previously encountered could return, along with the emotions that accompanied that extremely poor day. Your golfing behaviour, thoughts and feelings pick up just where you left off, producing uncertainty, doubt, lack of concentration, tension, and ultimately again poor play.

The individual golfer then has a mental problem of eliminating negative thoughts which were created by negative results.

Although this inability to put something that you don't want to think about out of your mind is more typical of certain personality types, it affects all of us from time to time, depending upon our day-to-day circumstances.

An example of the negative suggestion is as follows. Suppose that we give you the instruction, 'Don't think of an elephant!' Now obviously many will think immediately of an elephant.

Similarly, a poor hole and a poor round is an unpleasant experience and likely to remain imbedded in one's mind although it is a negative impression.

How can you stop thinking about that elephant? A remarkably successful way is to replace the elephant with another, different thought. For example, think of a zebra. But, how can you apply this solution to the game of golf? In other words, how can you stop thinking about hitting into water or into the woods?

At the end we will describe five specific exercises you can perform which will help you to break this feedback cycle when it becomes negative for you. But first we will also go farther to help you.

In order to be relaxed and mentally ready for golf, it is necessary to store as many positive suggestions into your mind as you possibly can. We are talking specifically about the unconscious mind which operates much like a computer and stores suggestions that are fed into it. As positive suggestions are fed in they have a cumulative effect and will last for long periods of time; that is, they will affect behaviour for a very long period of time. This 'exercise' technique consists of two steps, *relaxation* and *repetition*.

We know now that when the body is relaxed the mind is much more receptive to suggestions. This is what makes relaxation so important, not just on the course but also off the course. If you can take a few minutes in which you can close your eyes and relax, this is the ideal time for your mind to receive the suggestions that you wish to put into it.

A golfer who has had a particularly bad day on the course can almost always be found to have preceded his play with a hectic schedule in which little time was taken out for relaxation, concentration and the accumulation of positive suggestions. Therefore, we are going to suggest a technique in which positive suggestions may be stored that will have an effect upon extended play.

The second 'exercise' involved in putting suggestions into the mind is repetition. Just as in physical exercise, this mental exercise must be performed over and over and over again. This means that the positive suggestions must be delivered with repetition. In other words, they must be delivered repetitively and the best way to do this is to connect the repetition with the relaxation. When these two conditions are present, the mind power is at its best and mental exercise programme will be successful.

We will now review a series of exercises to improve concentration and mental readiness. The first and most important exercise is the systematic use of direct suggestions. Every golfer can apply this method by thinking of all of the positive things that he wants to accomplish on the golf course and writing them out in long hand.

Some examples of positive thoughts now follow, in order to give the reader an idea of some of the suggestions that have worked for us:

'You will hit the ball long and strong.'

'You will be mentally eager and ready at all times.'

'You will always play your best.'

'You will look forward to hard shots.'

'You will be confident at all times.'

'You will score well on this hole.'

'You will hit the ball in the air where water and sand are not present.'

You will notice that these suggestions are all written in the second person. The reason for this is that you will want to sit down with a cassette tape recorder and tape record the suggestions that we have given you here as well as those that you have written for yourself. When you do this speak slowly and in a dull monotonous voice. Record as many suggestions as you can. Be sure and make them positive!

If you want to be sure that the suggestions will improve your play as much as possible, include the following on your list and on your tape:

'When you see the fairway from the first tee, you'll remember all the good things you've first heard.'

Once you have made the tape you can sit down with your head back in an easy chair or lie down and relax while you listen to the suggestions. You will be relaxed and you will be open to the suggestions as they enter your mind. The more you play this tape and more suggestions that you put on the tape the more likely you will be to build up your confidence and your mind power.

A second exercise starts with you going back in time to the day that you were at your best. Pick out a time when you were hitting the ball especially well and think about this day over and over, many, many

30

times! Try to recapture the thoughts and feelings that you had that day. Take yourself around all 18 holes of the course remembering and thinking and concentrating upon every shot that you took that day.

That round of golf can become a model to which you can return, visually and mentally, whenever you need it for encouragement and for confidence building.

You can relive these shots and key rounds of golf while preparing to go out on the course, while actually playing golf and even when you are miles away from the golf course during the work day.

A third exercise that is especially beneficial is to move slower than you are accustomed to. Most of us rush around in the everyday course of events and are constantly on edge whether we realize it or not. Tension and anxiety build up without us really knowing that it is happening.

This build-up can cause us to do things that we would not do if we had taken the time to think and plan our actions carefully.

An excellent example of how this happens is the behaviour of the typical motorist in the traffic jam during rush hour or on a holiday weekend. Frustration leads to temper tantrums and childish behaviour.

When this happens to a golfer he has lost everything. He has lost his concentration, he cannot relax and he cannot play up to his capabilities.

It is especially important to maintain control and to 'stay on top of' ourselves. One of the best techniques to accomplish this is simply to move more slowly. Walk slower, speak slower, think things through more slowly and swing your club more slowly.

Many weekend golfers swing too hard trying to kill the ball. If you slow down your backswing and you follow through you may be amazed at the difference. In reality you will not be swinging nearly as slowly as you *think* you are swinging. You will find a new control and surprising power. Whenever you feel tension or pressure simply slow down your movements and you will be master of your fate.

The fourth exercise is based on a well-established fact and psychological principle, that of modelling. We recommend that the golfer select another golfer whose skills he respects. This golfer will then serve as a model, primarily for inspiration rather than for someone to copy.

The model does not have to be a professional golfer. In fact, if the

31

golfer who chooses a model selects a professional whom he does not know personally or has never watched this person, it may be difficult for him to identify with the model.

For most golfers it is preferable to select someone whom they know personally, at least a golfer whom they have followed at a tournament. It is very important to select someone who you think practises the mental side of the game as well as the physical side of the game. Be very careful to select someone who is mentally ready and even-tempered.

Once you have selected a model that you respect, it is easy to use this person as a reservoir to help you build up your own abilities.

Before you head for the golf course for each round of golf you should ask yourself, 'How would my model prepare for a game today?' Whenever you are faced with a pressure putt or a crisis shot you should ask yourself the question, 'How would my model handle this situation?'

It is very important to do this for critical shots, but it is even more important to incorporate this procedure into your daily mental practice as you prepare for every round of golf you play.

Once you ask yourself the questions you should answer them by talking to yourself and through visual imagery. Picture in your mind's eye how your model *would* handle the situation. Then picture in your mind how you *will* handle it.

Your picture should be as detailed as possible. You should strive to create a sequence of pictures much like a movie or video tape recall.

This brings us to the fifth and final exercise which is a series of steps that we recommend for you to follow whenever you play a round of golf.

First you should warm up mentally. How do you do this? You can simply play the direct suggestion tape that you have made while you close your eyes and relax in a chair or lie down for a few moments (anywhere from several to 30 minutes). As you are relaxed, listen to this expanded tape. If it is impossible for you to do this, at least you can close your eyes and repeat some suggestions that you have given yourself spontaneously.

Second, you should leave early for the golf course. Always give yourself plenty of time to get to the course. If you are accustomed to leaving an hour before you tee off, you should give yourself at least 30 extra minutes from now on.

Third, if you drive a car to the course, you should drive your automobile more slowly than you are accustomed. Drive at least 10 miles per hour less than your usual cruising speed.

Fourth, once you arrive at the clubhouse, dress more slowly and more carefully. If you are already dressed and do not use a clubhouse, at the very least you will put on your golf shoes and go through other favourite rituals before you begin play. Do this more slowly and more deliberately than you have ever done before. While you do it repeat some of your favourite suggestions to yourself.

Finally, at all times while warming up, while getting ready to leave, while driving to the course and finally while preparing to tee off, you should be thinking about your game and about your approach for the day.

You should focus on your best shots in the past and you should relive your best round of golf in the past. You should take yourself mentally in your mind's eye around the course and picture the middle of the fairway and the centre of the greens.

If you do this carefully each time you get ready for a round of golf and if you follow the other four exercises that we have suggested you will learn how to relax.

You will improve your concentration more than you thought was possible.

You will develop more and more self-confidence and you will increase your mind power, all of which will allow you to play better and more consistent golf than you ever have before in your life.

CHAPTER 6

No Way to Treat a Body

It is usually considered that success and affluence are accompanied by an unhealthy life style. At least it is felt that the greater the affluence, and the high-powered or glamorous circles in which people move, the harder it is to avoid drink, cigarettes or even drugs. Speaking as a golfer who travels the world and has the opportunity to move in these sort of circles, I must put another viewpoint: the more affluent people are, the more chance they have of ordering their own lives exactly as they require.

My acquaintance with smoking was very short-lived. It came about when I was young and impressionable—or should I say, wanting to impress—and I had bought an Austin-Healey sports car. The car looked beautiful to me. It had a bit of style, and I thought I would also get a nice English check cap and a pipe. In this way I would really look the part.

I spent one day with my nice Austin-Healey, in my nice English hat and my nice English pipe—and the next morning I woke up with the foulest taste in my mouth that I had ever known. It wasn't just an unpleasant *taste*, like medicine; my mouth and throat and lungs had been contaminated by nicotine. The thought of waking up each morning with this taste in your mouth was enough to make me throw away the pipe there and then.

Smoking, I will come back to, after considering alcohol. I have had a couple of bad experiences with drinking. The worst was in New Zealand, during a very strenuous tour that involved something like 28 matches in 31 days. I was with a couple of English professionals, and I remember one of them saying, "Tonight I'll get so drunk that I'll have to crawl home." Well, I got so drunk that I couldn't even crawl. They had to carry me home.

I vaguely recall demanding, "Give me the strongest in the house."

35

I think I took whisky, gin and brandy at various times. In the end I was desperately sick, unable to stop vomiting repeatedly. It is no fun to vomit repeatedly and helplessly, and to know what they mean when they say, "As sick as a dog."

I mean no disrespect to dogs, but the feeling of being sub-human is a shocking one. And you look back at yourself in disbelief. Was that *me*? Was that my idea, is that anyone's idea, of a good time?

It only needed an experience like this to confirm what I had seen with my eyes as a child. With no mother after the age of eight, and with my father working at the mine, I had the chance to wander around; and in a mining community there was of course quite a lot of pub life. The drunks and the alcoholics struck a note of horror in me. I thought these people might as well be dead. Not that I anticipated that I might become an alcoholic. But as a golfer I had a particular reason to keep my nerves sound. In such a slow, deliberate game, hitting a stationary ball in an atmosphere often of great tension, the nerves have to be rock solid.

I still occasionally have a beer, or a whisky—more often than not when it would be discourteous to refuse it. But I am myself very wary of drinking, because I have seen it ruin people's lives. I also realise that there are a vast number of people who drink in moderation and enjoy it. Many team sports, like rugby, would lose most of their social attraction if there was no drinking. And it has certainly been argued, in scientific studies, that people who drink in moderation tend to live longer than people who don't drink at all. But as far as I know, no one has dared to try the same argument for smoking.

There seems no doubt to me that *one* cigarette a day will have a negative effect on your health, no matter how small, and that two cigarettes will *double* this effect.

They say that it only needs a visit to a lung cancer ward to put anyone off smoking for life. I've been lucky, if that is the word, to have had a similar experience.

It was in 1973 that I had my only serious term in hospital. My kidneys weren't feeding the bladder properly, and the blockage of the connecting ureter had caused some kidney damage. An operation to rectify this was followed by a convalescent period which was often uncomfortable. Any movement which tensed the abdominal area brought acute pain.

There I was, lying on the bed on my back, in a ward with half a dozen fellow sufferers, and every time I had phlegm in my throat and tried to clear it I couldn't do it. It was too painful.

I lay there and asked myself how was it possible that someone who was so fit couldn't clear his throat. At any rate, I soon had reason to count my blessings. The fellows next to me were smokers. And whereas I could resist the urge to clear my throat, they couldn't stop themselves coughing. I will never forget the strange howl as these men started to cough and then cried. Sometimes it would go on and on, like someone trying to crank-start a car.

I knew how sore my own throat had become; I could only begin to imagine what they felt like with their smoker's coughs, and I thanked God I was not a smoker.

Millions of man-hours are lost in industry, and millions of pounds are spent by health services on avoidable, self-inflicted illness. But to the individual like myself the ultimate justification for keeping one's body free of abuse is the simple pleasure of being able to wake up and enjoy each morning.

I remember, when recovering from my operation, the joy of going for my first walk outside. I wasn't walking very comfortably, but any physical discomfort was transcended by the sight of doves on the roof of the beautiful, quaint little hospital, and the blue of the sky. In South Africa the sky is a deep, pure blue. Just as vivid were the green leaves on the trees. And I said a prayer to God, thanking Him for letting me appreciate good health.

In many ways, that period in hospital had a profound impact. Not least, it made me appreciate so basic a function as passing water. I daresay everyone, at some time or another, has experienced the frustration of not being able to get to the toilet—and *oh the relief* when you do! But this was nothing compared with the eight days in which I had to get along with a tube and a plastic bag.

It so happened that I gained my "freedom" on a Sunday. As I went to the toilet a service was in progress in the hospital's little chapel. And the church organ was playing as I passed water. It may sound ludicrous but it was an extraordinarily beautiful moment. It was also rather odd. Who on earth ever thinks that they're *lucky* to pass water?

But then who of us, as we eat with knife and fork, think that we're lucky to have two hands?

Anyhow, I told the nurse of my wonderful experience, and she said that as a matter of fact that church organ had been on loan and it was going to have to go back. As a hospital, she said, they couldn't buy an organ. I asked her how much it would cost. She said, something like 1,100 Rand (£600). I told her that they should buy a church organ and I would pay for it. I was more than happy to have the chance of expressing my gratitude.

How do you stop children from drinking and smoking? Just saying "*No*" or "*Don't*" is hardly likely to produce the desired result, especially because youngsters seem to find an attraction, or a challenge, in the forbidden deed. Hopefully, parents can lead by example, and if this is underpinned by love and respect there must be a good chance of the teaching getting through. But we realised that in our family there were also some special hazards, posed by a comparatively comfortable standard of living, the opportunity to travel, and indeed the fact that I myself was away a good deal of the time.

We decided to offer our children a "bargain". If when they reach the age of 21 they have neither drunk alcohol nor smoked, we will give them each a cheque for 1,000 Rand, and if they have abstained when they reach 25 they will each get a new car.

Let me come back now to the main theme of this chapter. Let's consider the word *abuse*. It is a strong word. It clearly indicates action —or inaction—which is reprehensible. No decent person would condone the abuse of property, the abuse of trust, the abuse of authority. . . . And yet many of us abuse our own bodies. The Bible declares that we should treat the body "as a holy temple", and that for me says it all. But even if there were no Bible, nor even a moral code, the same idea would hold good as a No. 1 principle.

CHAPTER 7

Secrets of a Travelling Man

When I'm really on the move, the scale of the travelling and of the work schedule must rival any businessman; and probably more so. Take, for example, one day before the 1978 British Open. At my home in Johannesburg I was up at 6 o'clock to see my horses train. After a shower and breakfast I met our best South African boxer, Kallie Knoetzer, who had wanted to come and talk with me. That was followed by a visit by some Japanese businessmen, the result of my having played a lot in Japan and having a strong feeling for that country. Then I had to rush into the city to do a television commercial. After that there was a Press conference where my attendance was vital, because we were announcing a new golf course project.

The Press conference finished at 3.30, and after the 20-minute drive home I had to pack and get to the airport by 6 o'clock to catch the London plane.

After a 15-hour flight I had an appointment at the Royal Automobile Club in London for a cocktail session followed by a talk. After that I was taken by helicopter to a golf club, to do a public relations day. On one such day, in Indianapolis, I had to play the same hole 44 times, with 44 different foursomes! This time I simply had to play a man on his home golf course, in front of a crowd who didn't know that I had never seen the course before or had travelled overnight from South Africa.

When this was done I had to get to King's Cross station in London, to catch the overnight train to Dundee. A fine start for the British Open. But not unusual, at that.

Why by train? In the first place, because I love train travel. It's a happy memory for me of the times as a young boy when I was taken by my mother and father once a year down to the coast by train. And today when I go to my farm, 375 miles from Johannesburg, I always take the train. We can all get in the train, the whole family, and we take a barrel of chicken with us. I love to look at the farms and at the country. The other reason I go by train—and it's part of the first reason—is that it's a chance to relax.

When travelling overseas you get used to being away from your own car, and perhaps it is a good thing too. And it seems quite clear to me that a businessman would do much more paper work on a train—possibly also have time for a nap—and arrive at his destination ready to get moving.

Of course, most of the time I am travelling very large distances, and therefore flying. South Africa to America; America to Japan; America to England. But the same principle holds good. Someone else is transporting you; therefore you can make what you like of the time. I try to use the whole journey time to rest and prepare my body for the strain of the time change on the other side.

Contrary to what people think, one doesn't get used to such travelling; the more you do the worse it gets. But there are ways to counteract it. If you sleep well you have a big asset, and fortunately for me the fact that I am on a plane makes me want to sleep. Invariably there is one other person in the row of seats with me and I say to him, "Would you like to have the seats?" He says he would, and I tell him that he can have the seats and I'll have the floor. I sleep at his feet, virtually.

In fact when I travel first class I still usually end up on the floor, though I can also sleep upright in my seat—I only have to put my head back into the pillow. Particularly when I'm on the floor, I'm likely to sleep practically the whole distance of a long trip—for example, Los Angeles to Tokyo—and very often the hostess wakes me and asks me if I'm feeling all right. Someone has evidently thought I might be dead.

The fact is I sleep everywhere on the floor. In hotels. Even at home. It helps to keep the back straight. I believe this is a very important aid to good health, though it is especially important for someone who spends a lot of time on his feet playing golf, which makes the back sore.

There is a "programme" on planes the staff follow, and so do most of the passengers. It consists of something like cocktails in the first hour, then a meal, then a film . . . I avoid this. I tell them what I want when I get on the plane. I take out the eyeshade which I keep with me when travelling, and get my head down. I don't know how you calculate such a thing, but I'm sure that the ability to sleep has been a great factor in keeping me going so strongly.

On planes, many people eat and drink a lot, and smoke, mainly to pass the time. I would dread the thought of arriving at my destination feeling as awful as many of them will feel. You *know* that when you arrive your stomach isn't going to be the same, so why not make things easier for it? The best thing to eat, if anything, is fruit, and the best thing to drink is water. In this kind of air pressure the body becomes dehydrated, so I always try to drink plenty of water when flying. I often manage to take on some fruit with me. There is no law against taking food into the cabin and dried fruit is easy to handle.

When you arrive, the rule is *not* to sleep. Instead, "get on the clock" and pretend you're having a normal day on local time. By night-time, you'll be exhausted and you'll almost certainly sleep well. By contrast, if you sleep on arrival, you probably won't be ready for another spell at night, and you'll only toss and turn.

When I get to my hotel I like to soak in a hot bath and follow this with a cold shower—or vice versa. I feel that this gets the circulation moving.

If you're a jogger this is a wonderful way to get the body moving, with a slow, easy workout. I believe that a mechanism which is encouraged to work moderately hard will adjust much quicker than one which does nothing.

This is surely true not only of adjusting to time changes after intercontinental flights, but also to the changes involved in moving house, or your job, visiting relatives or going on holiday.

After my bath and shower I like to go straightaway to the golf course and practise. The most important part of this is getting air in the lungs, getting the blood pulsing, the body moving and, as I say, getting immediately "on the clock". I have a normal evening meal that night but I always make sure I eat plenty of roughage. This means All Bran, prunes or other fruit at breakfast, especially in the first couple of days, and it means my trusty ally, Mealie Meal, at any time of the day.

Mealie Meal is the black man's name for a rough maize, to which he adds water and boils up into a porridge. It's the African's staple diet and it's my staple standby. I think it's delicious and I take it with me everywhere. In hotels I borrow an electric saucepan that I can plug into a socket in the bedroom to boil it up.

Another faithful companion is my herbal tea. This is tannin-free and caffein-free, and I carry these little bags around so that I can always contrive to have my own tea. I've learnt to be firm but polite about my own tea. Too bad if my host or hostess might think I'm a little cranky; too bad if the head steward on the Flying Scotsman tries to insist that I'll have no room for complaint with the cup of tea he serves. I take the trouble to explain that these tea bags of mine have no tannin or caffein, and if they would be so kind as to bring me just a pot of boiling water I would be very grateful.

Now, I confess that a normal cup of tea would not taste unpleasant, though it certainly wouldn't be as nice as my own tea—which, by the way, is a farmers' tea and therefore a touch of home.

I would like to think that this is yet another factor in keeping my nerves in good condition, and in sleeping well. Exactly what the degrees are in this I wouldn't know, but when I think of all the cups of tea and coffee the other guys must drink over the years, that seems an awful lot of caffein and tannin going into the system.

To explain my feelings I can do no better than quote this truest of sayings: "Perfection is no little thing, but little things make perfection."

When I'm on the move, I make particularly sure to keep up my exercises. Mostly this is done in the hotel room. I swing a special, heavy club, and I also use this to strengthen my fingers. A weighted shoe is another part of the baggage: this increases the effect of leg exercises, and it also gives the wrists some work to do as they wind it up and down. For my lower backbone I do a pelvic tilt exercise which involves lying on my back and flexing the pelvis upwards, with the cheeks of the buttocks clenching together. For the arms I do dynamic tension work, pressing my hand hard against the wall as if hitting a golf ball. For the legs I spring up and try to touch the ceiling. Best of all, I run on the spot. This might involve 300 steps, and I try to get the knees at least up to waist height.

How many businessmen follow a routine like that? One of the answers, I know, is "I just don't have any time for exercise." To that, I say Hogwash. You can always find time if you make it a priority in the day.

I don't believe there is anyone, from heads of state to hard-worked general practitioners, who don't have—or can't make—a spare 20 minutes in the day. What about lunchtime? Does a businessman go out for lunch every single day? Why not go to a gymnasium two or three times a week, and go out to lunch on the other days? It will be probably found that there is more time for work, and more work done, on the "gymnasium days".

I've said that exercise must be regarded as a priority. This is the point. It's a priority because it's *that* important. And it shows a return even in the short-term. It means more energy to put into business.

Another argument that many people make, especially those in business, is that they need to drink at the end of the day to "relax". I say that that's just an attitude of mind, it's the easy answer. I know, and practise, several other ways of winding down. One of these is jogging, or running on the spot. Another is a long, hot bath. Another is simply to sit down and close your eyes. This last is almost a form of yoga. Even waiting just a few minutes for a phone call I'll lay on the floor and close my eyes, almost doze off. I'll try to make my mind a complete blank, or fill it with pleasant thoughts of my family and my farm. I don't need a drink, or a pill, to relax.

But, if asked to prescribe a programme for a busy executive, I wouldn't necessarily ask for a drink to be cut out. And I wouldn't crack a whip at a training track. It's really a matter of being realistic, and looking for something which stands a fair chance of being carried out.

Foodwise, I would recommend first of all that he stops eating bread. This may seem difficult, and I know how big these little sacrifices sometimes seem. If this *is* too tough, I would suggest one piece of brown bread toast at breakfast.

Bacon and eggs should be eaten very seldom; certainly not every day. Butter intake should be reduced.

Make a point of taking more roughage at breakfast. Include more fruit and vegetables in the daily diet, and more salads (without lashings of dressing). Try to drink de-caffeinated coffee and tea.

As for exercise, make a point first thing in the morning of running-in-place. Start with 50 steps (for the *very* unfit, 20) and gradually build up to 300.

And join a health club or gymnasium, so that you can workout for at least 20 minutes, at least two lunch-times a week. Follow this by a hot and cold shower, and a light lunch.

Pressure and strain are factors central to everything we are discussing in this chapter. We are saying that through fitness we can help keep strain at bay. But of course, mental stress can be combated, as it were, on its own terms. A fit body can help the nervous system, but a sensible *attitude* is also important. It may sound obvious, but the fact is that frustration and tension is often of our own making, and therefore avoidable.

I'm no different from anyone else. I get irritable. It happens most of all when I'm all set to go and do something, especially practise, and something else comes along to distract me. People can be very demanding, and I can't be rude. But very often these feelings of irritation and frustration are helped by a discipline acquired from golf.

When you miss a shot in golf, as any professional will tell you, nobody in the world can give you that shot over again. Once you've missed it, it's 2,000 years ago. And many times I've missed a putt on the last green that's been worth many thousands of dollars.

This helps me when, for example, I hear that one of my horses has died. I ask my manager if it was caused by negligence. He may say no, the horse just died. I establish that there is nothing else that can be done, nothing to be learnt from this unfortunate experience. And finally you just have to say, "All right, thanks for telling me." End of conversation.

It helps particularly also in a situation that is well known to me, as a constant traveller, but which is also a common experience for most people. That is when your car, or taxi, is held up in heavy traffic; or when the train is running late; or when you're standing in a queue. At these times I try to ask myself: "Now is there anything else you could do that you're not doing?" Usually the answer is No. You *can't* pick up the car and lift it over the traffic. So if the answer is No, you have to tell yourself to sit back and relax.

We must remember that everything comes from that little brain-box.

This is a much bigger statement than it may sound. It means that the cause and cure of such problems aren't the other cars in the traffic jam, or the other people who are upsetting you. It's that little brain-box from which all these feelings and messages have originated: that's the only point of communication which can help you, so you'd better speak to it directly.

CHAPTER 8

A Doctor Named Cooper

It was about 1970 when I first heard of a doctor named Cooper, who operated a clinic in Dallas which tested people's fitness, and my first reaction was to want to see just what my fitness rating was. Eventually I had the chance to do this, and in May of 1971 I was tested at the now famous Cooper Clinic.

I received a stress electrocardiograph by being put to work on a powered treadmill, in a test which is designed to get you to maximum exertion. To put it more bluntly, you're pushed to exhaustion—though this isn't quite as bad as it sounds for very unfit people, because they simply get puffed, or their legs let them down, and they stop before they can over-exert themselves.

A fitter person like myself can cope with more stress, and in fact Dr. Cooper's report says that for me "this appeared to be a sub-maximal test". I walked for 25 minutes, during the course of which electrodes plugged on my chest were providing a continuous record of heart-rate, and blood pressure was also being recorded. All the figures, during exercise and during recovery, are shown in the box on page 48.

The duration of my walk—25 minutes—has been exceeded by only 3 per cent of those who've been tested at the clinic. In a separate test of lung performance the vital capacity figure was 4.5 litres compared with the predicted figure (according to age, weight, etc.) of 4.0 litres. The opinion of the clinic was that the lung-capacity and treadmill tests indicated "a superb condition, not only for a golfer, but for a runner". At this time, at age 35, I was running regularly, and the clinic reported an "outstanding aerobics response".

Aerobics is Dr. Cooper's term, now understood fairly universally. But at that stage I was learning, too. At his clinic he isn't concerned so much with testing athletes as with measuring and monitoring ordinary people. Dr. Cooper is a cardiologist dedicated to the idea of trying to combat heart disease with exercise. Specifically, with aerobic exercise

47

(exercise which depends on oxygen and, by demanding a constant supply of this fuel, creates a training effect which benefits lungs and heart).

That was the message which I rapidly absorbed the first time I heard Dr. Cooper speak, in Jacksonville, Florida. It was a most inspiring address. Also present were some students from one of the universities, and they finally walked out almost starry-eyed.

Dr. Cooper gained much of his experience from working with the US Air Force, and one of the stories he told was of three men who were candidates for a special project. One man only was required and had to

---

STANDARD STRESS TEST

Name: Gary Player. Place: Cooper Clinic. Date: 23rd May 1971.

EXERCISE		RECOVERY	
Mins	**Heart-Rate**	**Mins**	**Heart-Rate**
1	90	1	140
5	98	3	108
10	120	5	98
15	140	10	88
20	158		
25	176		

(Predicted maximum: 185)

Blood pressure at commencement: 110/80

Blood pressure after 10 mins recovery: 120/80

---

be in top physical condition. One of these three candidates took no regular exercise; one rode his bike to the air base and back each day, about three miles each way; the other, who was distinctly muscular, did isometric and weight-training exercises for one hour a day, five days a week.

The three were given a treadmill test to determine their powers of endurance. The non-exerciser was fatigued within the first five minutes, and so was the weightlifter! The cyclist was still going strong after 15 minutes, and was chosen for the project.

The aerobic fitness that this chap had gained from cycling was the sort you need to get you through the physical stress of everyday life—from shovelling snow to simply working long hours.

But the most impressive story told by Dr. Cooper, and it's stayed in my mind ever since, was the case of a 30-year-old Starfighter pilot. One night at home he felt a tight sensation in his chest, a bit like indigestion or heartburn, but slightly different. He tried to shrug it off by doing a few exercises, but couldn't. As it happened, he had to have his annual physical check two days later, and his electrocardiograph showed what is termed "inverted T waves". Permanent grounding was an almost automatic consequence for the unfortunate pilot, who saw this as the end of the road.

In subsequent interviews, the pilot revealed that his father had died at 27 and one of his uncles in his thirties, possibly both of them from heart conditions.

The future looked bleak but the pilot, when introduced to Dr. Cooper, was more than keen to be directed into an exercise programme. First, he stopped smoking. Then he started with walking, gradually progressing up to one mile a day. Soon he was running on his own, steadily increasing the distance. Finally he ran the 26-mile marathon.

Meanwhile, however, the Air Force medical board was unwilling to give the pilot back his flying status. Perhaps they were just unable to believe that such an alarming medical condition could be rectified. An ECG had been run again on the pilot and, in being pushed to exhaustion, he had broken every record on Cooper's treadmill. Neither this, nor the marathon, was able to impress the medical board—until Cooper arranged a coronary angiogram.

This is an examination of the coronary arteries from *inside* them, by inserting a catheter in the large artery of the left arm. The picture gained by the examining doctor was most impressive. The arteries were larger than expected, judged by the size of the heart, and his physical status was put at "excellent".

Backed by this report, the pilot at last got his grounding order lifted by the medical board.

You sometimes hear it said that, while the arguments for exercise sound pretty good, nobody has proved that exercise makes you live any longer. Maybe we're going to have to wait a long time before we establish rock-solid proof. But why wait that long, when we know stories like this pilot's, and many other stories of rehabilitation—and of hundreds of other experiments and studies which all point in the same direction?

In any case, why worry about trying to prove that exercise makes you live longer, when we know that it adds vitality to the life you are living?

Dr. Cooper describes in his talks how he has helped people with diabetes, with ulcers, with lung ailments, with arthritis and with various forms of depression. In addition, that is, to cardiac problems.

I know from my own experience that when I'm fit my reflexes and sense of touch are heightened, my eyesight is better and so is my hearing. Of course I'm talking as a "sports specialist", whose work is very demanding and very exacting, and causes me to notice the "fine tuning". But I'm sure that the effect of exercise is even more profound for those who are comparatively unathletic.

I'm sure that one of the great arguments for exercise—and it may also mean life-saving, ultimately—is that it helps to defeat boredom. It creates purpose, discipline, excitement in lives which can otherwise be dull and monotonous.

Yet if the average man or woman goes to the family doctor and says they're thinking of taking up exercise, will they get enthusiastic support? Or will they instead receive encouragement to "take it easy" from a GP who is himself overweight, who drinks and smokes, and doesn't take exercise?

I'm afraid that the average doctor can sometimes be the worst person to go to for advice on physical fitness. He's part of an ill-health system, in that he reacts to illness, usually with a bottle of pills, instead of getting to the root cause. How much better to work to *prevent* ill health.

I only wish there were 10 Dr. Coopers in every country in the world. You may say to yourself, "So what's so special about America? Isn't it the land of the automobile, the hamburger and the big medical bills?" The fact is, things have been changing.

Accordingly I asked Dr. Cooper himself to summarise the present position and he kindly responded as follows:

"Since 1940 there had been an alarming increase in the USA of deaths from coronary disease. At one time it had reached epidemic proportions. By 1960, nearly 2,000,000 heart attacks were occurring each year, and over 700,000 deaths.

"Starting in the mid-to-late 1960s there was a great interest in exercise, and by 1978 it was estimated that the number of regular joggers in the USA had risen to as many as 25 million. Critics anticipated that this jogging boom might bring a significant increase in sudden deaths. Yet, to the contrary, every year since the mid-to-late sixties there has been a decrease in heart-attack deaths. Recent statistics indicate that heart deaths in 1978 will be 28 per cent down on the 1968 figures.

"As there is more than one cause of heart disease, it is not possible to say that exercise is the major factor in this reduction; but it is obvious that the highly significant increase in exercise participation has *not* resulted in an increase in deaths from heart attacks. Further, there is increasing evidence that it is possible to lessen one's coronary risk as the result of a regular physical conditioning programme. In other words, the results are too impressive to be ignored.

"It would also appear that the youth addiction towards alcohol in the 1950s, and drugs in the 1960s, is being replaced by jogging in the 1970s. If this is so, it is the most important change of the past century towards better health.

"With all the information we now have about the value of exercise, we must ask seriously whether people can afford *not* to exercise."

To Dr. Cooper's careful summing-up I would like to add two observations of my own, from South Africa. The first is that the black man rarely seems to fall victim of a heart attack. The second is that white women, who are clearly spared a great deal of domestic work, suffer more heart attacks than women anywhere else in the world. It is interesting that women in general have a much lower incidence of heart disease than men. Nevertheless, as I have said, the incidence is higher for South African women.

Indeed, study of the two races in South Africa provides a very interesting medical story. In the words of the Hans Snyckers Institute:

"Two large races arrived here at the same time, they have lived side-by-side for more than three centuries, they have remained true to their own way of living, and the pattern of diseases in each group is totally different from the other. The $3\frac{3}{4}$ million white South Africans suffer from the diseases of the Western world, often in extreme degree. The 15 million black inhabitants do *not* suffer the diseases most common in the West: coronary heart disease, appendicitis, peptic ulcer . . ."

Perhaps most interesting of all, the Institute observes that in *other* countries the black races have become completely westernised in their disease patterns:

"The US Negro shows the same high incidence of Western diseases as the US White, and in some instances he surpasses the races of Europe in his manifestations of Western complaints."

Finally, I must say once again that I find the work of Dr. Cooper an inspiration. When we talk of the heart, the medical "stars" of the last decade have been the transplant surgeons. I realise that to make progress we have to accept slow progress—and that is certainly how it seems when the recipient of a new heart lives for a few months, maybe a couple of years, and then dies. As I say, I accept this is the way of progress. But to my mind the accolades and the publicity should go to those whose efforts are directed to saving, or transforming, the lives of thousands.

When I say thousands, let me be more explicit. Up to the end of 1978, 25,000 people had received a treadmill ECG at the Cooper Clinic. Hundreds of thousands more had been influenced by his world-famous book, *Aerobics.* I find this very exciting. It makes me wish that I could have a second career, as a doctor specialising in the prevention of heart attacks.

To entertain thousands of people through sport, is one thing. But to physically improve the lives of millions is something else altogether. Perhaps the future will provide me with the chance to make something out of this very nice dream.

CHAPTER 9

The Jogging Golf Pro

It caused a bit of amusement on the tour, to start with, when I emerged from my hotel room in jogging kit; and probably some puzzlement or consternation when I followed a tournament round, and a spell on the practice tee, by running around the golf course. The golfers and the golf writers who did find this odd or amusing may have modified their view over the subsequent years.

I certainly had no reason to be anything but grateful as, at the age of 42, I walked the uphill last hole of the Masters in 1978. When you're fit an uphill stretch like that feels much the same as flat ground. And the records of professional golf tournaments are full of the stories of ageing or overweight stars who have faded on the last day, or in a play-off; and there are some not able to play a series of tournaments without needing a break.

There is no question that the difference between exercising and not exercising will be clearly felt during a tournament. I'm talking specifically about stamina, and also about general good health. I've only got to consider one of my horses on the farm—for the horse is the ultimate athlete—and how even a very short lay-off visibly affects its condition.

It is also a medical fact that if you hospitalise a person, if you confine him to bed, the body reacts adversely: the muscles start to wither, the bones in time become brittle and thinner than normal, and the heart beats quicker and less efficiently. So I don't feel I need to apologise for my jogging on the golf tour!

I used to take my blue tracksuit and my Adidas training shoes with me on all my travels; and I've jogged in most countries of the world. I've jogged around many a motel block in the USA and, where the streets are a little too bustling, run *inside* hotels.

In Japan I used the long, long corridors of some of their huge hotels. In Paris I ran up and down the staircase of the George V hotel—all the way up and all the way down.

There's also another good reason for jogging like this. As I point out elsewhere in the book, it helps the body to adjust to travelling, time changes and different eating schedules.

During 1978, however, I suffered some back pain and decided to stop jogging for a while. I had an X-ray in Johannesburg and was told that I had a lower disc problem. The disc was pressing on the nerve, causing pain in the lower back and a bit of numbness in the leg. Although the problem was not at a serious level, I was told I must be careful, and do remedial exercises.

The temptation was to think that jogging caused this problem. But on longer reflection I realised it was probably created by a combination of factors. The main one was probably the golf swing itself, for striking the ball involves a savage whip and bend of the lower back that *must* be abnormal. There was also the fact that having got used to sleeping on hard beds or on the floor, I had then to sleep on some soft beds. And jogging on hard pavements must have aggravated the problem.

It could even be that the problem wasn't necessarily to do with golf, or with soft beds, or with jogging—and I want to dwell on this because a lot of people in sport do suffer lower back problems.

It is argued that one of the reasons for back trouble is that the main muscle which controls the pelvis tends to behave in an unhelpful way. When we take a lot of exercise—especially exercise like running—it tightens and shortens, pulling the lower back forward, tipping the pelvis downward and causing a "sway back". The hamstring muscles are then also affected, and may get aggravated.

The position is, ironically, the one we tend to get into when we pull our shoulders back and our stomach in; we also instinctively flex our pelvis backwards. The vertebrae curve more and bear down on each other.

People who have to stand for long periods can suffer in this way. The remedy is to do exercises which push the pelvis forward—frequently referred to in exercise manuals as "pelvic tilt" exercises.

Certainly I was advised to concentrate on these after I'd had my X-ray. I was told it was the best single exercise for the back. The movement is more apparent if you do it with your hands down over your hips, and you almost try to swivel your pelvis forward and up. You can pretend you're drawing pistols from hip holsters, or practising for a job as a belly dancer, or anything else you care to visualise! The simplest way to do it is lying down, perhaps with your hands underneath you so that you can feel the cheeks of your buttocks closing with each contraction; but I can now also do it when sitting down, standing still, and even when walking.

My problem seems to have been most aggravated by prolonged effort on hard surfaces. However, when I am on the farm I've made an effort to jog where otherwise I would walk. It might only be 100 yards here, 300 yards there, but it gets the heart working and it all adds up. When we go to the coast I run barefooted along the beach. And in hotel rooms I do a lot of running-in-place. Actually this last exercise can be quite strenuous, because I try to get my knees very high, and my legs certainly feel more muscular and stronger since I started doing it.

I hope to return to regular jogging, when I can get my back problem sorted out—though I may well try and avoid hard surfaces. I would also like to try to make the point that is is no use exercising and jogging if you don't watch your diet.

Nutrition-blindness is perhaps the most dire affliction of the Western life style. Why more golf professionals aren't alert to this I really don't know. There is one well-known name on the circuit, he's about 55 and a marvellous golfer, a man who is still very keen to do well, but he's 30 or 40 pounds overweight. If only he could get into shape he could still win.

There are also young men, fired up with ambition, who don't make the effort to lose a few, obviously surplus pounds. They'll practise at the golf course, they'll practise very hard because they're determined to be successful. And then defeat themselves in the cocktail lounge and the grill room. In fact it would do them more good to practise jogging and exercise, and discipline with the knife and fork, than all the golf practice they do.

Twenty-four hours with Player

Wife Vivienne, and daughters, meet Gary at Johannesburg Airport. The scene is a familiar one: it is evening, and he has just flown in from the USA.

The next morning, not being able to sleep any longer because of the time change, he gets up at 5 am. He wants to see his horses exercise. He also has to be at the airport, again, at 7 am to catch a flight to Port Elizabeth. There he will spend the day with the Ford company, whose vehicle he drives and for whom he does public relations days and golf clinics. Even the chauffeur has a Gary Player golf book requiring signature. The only quiet moments are provided by the flight to Port Elizabeth, though even in this time he has some reading to do. And always there are people—even children—anxious to talk to him and quick to ask for his autograph.

At Ford he lunches with the board. He is the centre of attention; all questions, and all talk, revolves around him. Lunch is followed by a one-hour photographic section in which he works his way through the entire range of Ford vehicles.

Now comes the section of the day which is probably most popular with Ford men, when they see action on the golf course with Gary Player. He plays three holes with three partners and then joins forces with another three. He talks about the different shots, his and theirs, and coaches as he goes. And, of course, always makes himself available for photographs. There will be more pictures at a cocktail party in the evening.

Player has the chance of an hour to himself. He uses it to practise, and sees out the last of the daylight hitting hundreds of golf balls. Then comes the cocktail session—at which he stays on the "soft stuff"—and after that films and a lecture. In this long day he never falters.

CHAPTER 10

Mysteries of The Future

All I can say about the future is that I have no idea what it holds, and I am not greatly concerned. All my physical application to date has been geared to the idea that I will continue playing professional golf for many years, but I don't *have* to. I could visualise the future holding out different opportunities, both in South Africa and abroad.

Certainly I know what I enjoy most in life. It is the complete happiness of being on the farm with my family. Of working on the farm with horses and dogs and tractors, baling hay, laying bricks, putting up fences. When I'm away there's never a day goes by that I don't think of it and yearn for it.

That doesn't necessarily mean that my future lies there. It is a matter that is in God's hands, and I happily accept this. But there is one thing I am sure about, and that is that if I was to stay on the farm and never play another round of golf—or to do anything else other than golf—I would keep working at my fitness. I certainly wouldn't drift from the standards I've established. For as long as I live I'll be constantly looking after myself.

I have such a zest for life, I enjoy life too much, to want to risk losing it. I know that when you're fit you enjoy every moment of life more—whether you're on a golf course, with your family, working on the farm, or sitting with your fellows and friends enjoying a chat and a joke.

When I'm riding a horse I think to myself, "Isn't this great!" I'm like a kid of 25. At 43 I can run and swim with my children, play football and tennis with them, practise handstands . . . No, sir, I would not want to risk giving this up.

People visualise themselves alone on a desert island. When I think of that I can't imagine *not* wanting to keep fit. I'd run and swim, and all the fruits would be a compensation for not being able to boil up the Mealie Meal! And I must admit that one of the reasons I'd keep in shape is because there would always be that chance of a boat coming by to pick me up.

The fact is, though, I'm not often lonely when I do have to be on my own. A desert island may be a fantasy, but there are "desert islands" in real life too, and none of us can be sure what lies ahead. I do know that optimism, enthusiasm and a sense of humour are essential ingredients, and I would guess that they have a much better chance of surviving in a fit body. Thus we give ourselves the chance to endure the worst that life can throw at us, or enjoy the best it has to offer us.

Advanced Fitness

Some suggestions were given earlier in the book for maintaining fitness in the course of day-to-day life. This was especially for those on the move—"convenience fitness", if you like. For those who have the opportunity, and want to make a more concentrated effort to get fit, a training framework is offered here.

It consists of four alternatives: jogging, swimming, stair-climbing and exercises. All these are activities intended to activate the heart and lungs. Decide on a combination that appeals to you most.

But, bear in mind there should be a minimum of three sessions per week, and that at least one of them should be jogging or swimming.

Jogging

A two-mile run is the aim. But you're advised to progressively work up to it in this manner:

Find a one-mile "course" which can be sub-divided with regularly spaced "reference points", like lamp posts or side streets along a straight road. Or, indeed, an athletic track with its quarter-mile laps.

Start by walking to one lamp post (or whatever) and jogging to the next. For the very unfit it could even be two sets of jogging to one of walking, but on the first outing a strictly even division should be maintained throughout.

Don't get carried away. Subse-quently, improve the ratio between run and walk sections to (for example) 2 and 1. Keep on increasing the ratio of run-to-walk sections in further outings *only* when the previous balance has been comfortably maintained throughout.

Continue the programme until one mile can be jogged non-stop and in reasonable comfort.

Now try to work up to the target of two miles. Be prepared to have walking breaks along the way, if need be. When the two miles can be run non-stop, comfortably, the basic exercise level has been reached. The distance, or the speed, can be increased—as can the frequency of the runs—but the basic level has been established.

For those interested in time, a decent jogging pace is something like 8–10 minutes per mile for men, 10–12 minutes for women (but age, and differences in individual fitness levels, alter such estimates enormously).

Swimming

The approach is much the same as in the jogging programme. Start by swimming single widths of the pool, in whatever stroke you can best manage. This will probably be breast-stroke. Allow at least a two-minute recovery between each crossing; in this interval kicking or other leg/hip exercises might be done against the pool wall.

When a number of widths can be swum comfortably in a session, graduate to lengths.

When a number of lengths, with rest intervals, can be swum comfortably, start to link them together.

The basic target (like the two-mile run in the jogging programme) is a continuous swim of 300 metres— nine lengths of most pools. This is likely to take 12–15 minutes doing breast-stroke.

As in jogging, the swimmer may well want to increase the distance or the speed. He also has the alternative of doing the same programme with a more difficult stroke.

Stair-climbing

Find a flight of stairs which provide 10 stairs in a straight line. A normal flight may more likely be about 13, but keep to 10 for this exercise.

Start at the bottom and go up and down five times to the minute. That means five times up and five times down. A watch, or clock, with a sweep second hand is a great asset, because it's essential to keep the speed steady at five flights to the minute.

Don't go faster just because it seems easy. The idea is to maintain an effort which can be kept up for several minutes.

Start by trying to go for, perhaps, two minutes. Aim to work up eventually to 10 minutes. Although this exercise is particularly suitable for a house-bound woman, men should *not* regard it as too simple for them.

Fifty flights in 10 minutes will make anyone feel he's had a thorough workout.

Exercise Session

The purpose of all the following exercises is to raise the pulse rate (as in jogging or swimming or stair-climbing) with effort which is *sustained* rather than abrupt or spasmodic. The aim should be to adjust one's approach and effort so that the movement can be repeated upwards of 20 times in the course of one "set". Three sets of each exercise should be done, with intervals for recovery.

1. Ski Jumps. Stand with feet together, hands by sides. Spring up and down off the balls of the feet in a lightly bouncing fashion to warm-up and then swing each foot alternately forwards and backwards with a rhythmic "skipping" tempo.

2. Leg Raising. Lie on back with arms by sides. Raise both legs (with knees slightly bent) to the vertical and then lower, raise again, and so on.

3. Sit-ups. Lie on back, hands behind head. Sit up to vertical position, keeping back as straight as possible, though knees can bend as necessary.

4(a). Half Push-ups. Lie on floor, hands flat beside chest as for normal push-up. Push up until arms are straight, but leave lower trunk on the floor. **Or:**

4(b). Elbow Push-ups. As above, but with the upper body supported by the elbows placed under the shoulders and forearms along the floor. Raise the body by straightening it from head to heels. **Or:**

4(c). Leaning Push-ups. Do the push-up at an angle of about 45 degrees, with the hands against the edge of a desk or shelf and the feet at least 3 ft back.

5. Burpees. From a standing position, go down into a crouch with the hands on the floor, then shoot legs backwards to the basic push-up position. Shoot the legs forward again to the crouch position, and then stand up. This is one "burpee". **Note:** This is far tougher than the other exercises. It should only be tried when progress has been made with the others, and even then only about 5–10 burpees need to be performed in each "set".

A Quarter Century of Player Victories

The ultimate proof of fitness and success lies in Gary Player's major tournament victories, which span 24 years and number over 100.

The following chronicle is not just a statistical list of Player's wins. The record demonstrates, again and again, mental and physical stamina overcoming the most extreme pressure. It could even be said that Player has proved he is at his best when the going is toughest.

In the chronicle, assembled by *The Sunday Times*, some details—especially yearly winning totals and world stroke averages—are available only from the mid-sixties. Other details such as prize money, course yardage, par, etcetera, are given where known.

In each tournament the scores of the runner-up (or *one* of them, where second place was shared) are given in brackets so as to provide some statistical comparison.

Bearing in mind exchange rate variations over three decades, a very rough guide for prize money figures is: £1 = 2 South African Rands = 2 Australian Dollars = 3 US Dollars.

1955

Egyptian Matchplay
April 15–17
Gezira Country Club, Cairo

In this, his first golfing stop on his first visit to Europe, Player beat his fellow South African Brian Wilkes, 2 and 1, and in the final Harold Henning (the favourite for the title held by Bobby Locke) by 5 and 4.

In the 36-hole final Player was 2-up after 18 holes scored in 67, and was eight strokes under par at the finish.

1956

East Rand Open
March 4–5
Benoni Country Club
Par 72

| Gary Player | 67–72–70–70: 279 |
| (A. Guthrie | 72–73–71–69: 285) |

Player's first round 67 was a course record; he had five birdies between holes 3 and 11 and scored the remaining 13 holes in par. Five strokes clear after two rounds, and seven ahead after three, he led the tournament throughout.

In the final round he dropped two shots at 16 but still finished an easy winner, with a tournament-record total.

South African Open
March 31–April 2
Durban Country Club
Par 73

| Gary Player | 72–71–72–71: 286 |
| (B. Keyter | 73–72–74–70: 289) |

At 20, Player became the youngest winner of the Open. He shared the lead with Dennis Hutchinson after the first round; otherwise he led from start to finish. His lead at the start of the last round was only one stroke, and he dropped a stroke at each of the first two holes, but soon picked up birdies and finished a surprisingly comfortable winner.

No one in the tournament broke 70, but all Player's rounds came close —and in fact all broke par. The 20-year-old made a big impression with the power of his driving and equally with his attacking chipping and putting.

UK Dunlop
May 1–4
Sunningdale Golf Club, Surrey
Par 72   6,500 yds

Gary Player	70–64–64–72–68: 338
	£500
(A. Lees	65–69–68–68–70: 340)

Player's total was thought to be the best anywhere for a five-round tournament, unusual though these are, and he beat the record for this particular event by seven strokes.

His second round was only one short of Norman von Nida's record, and when the last day started he was four ahead. He faltered in the morning and was two behind at one point, but in the final, afternoon round consolidated with sound, unspectacular golf over the brush and moorland course.

Meanwhile his 48-year-old rival Arthur Lees, the Sunningdale professional, lost shots at 15 and 17 as tiredness contributed to what was a most rare defeat for him on his home course.

Ampol Tournament

Nov 14–18
Yarra Yarra, Melbourne
Par 73

Gary Player   66–73–69–72: 280
£500
(B. Winninger   73–68–74–71: 286)

Player's opening 66 broke the course record by two strokes and gave him a four-stroke lead. This lead narrowed to two strokes after a second round played in rain and wind, in which he found the greens difficult. In a delayed third round—after the course had been flooded—most of his rivals faded, while accuracy around the greens kept him in front.

He led by seven going into the last round, finished nervously with his drive at the 18th hooked into trees, but recovered heroically to snatch an eagle—and tie the four-round record for the course.

1957

Ampol Tournament
Oct 31–Nov 2
Australian Club Course, Kensington
Par 72

Gary Player £800	74–70–66–71: 281
(D. Thomas	72–65–71–75: 283)

David Thomas held a three-stroke lead at the halfway stage, and Player was altogether seven strokes adrift. In the heat of the last day Thomas became uncomfortable; Player started steadily and rose to great heights.

In the morning round he played the homeward nine in 31, which included five birdies. In fact he did not drop a stroke on any hole of the final 36, while he gathered eight birdies. It was his second successive win in the Ampol.

Australian PGA
Nov 19–21
Huntingdale Golf Club, Melbourne
Par 73

In the final of this matchplay tournament, Player beat Peter Thomson 2-up. During the first 18 holes of the 36-hole final, Player was 3-down at the ninth and 2-down at the 18th. He then played the second 18 holes of this—Australia's longest course—in 67. He finished mentally and physically exhausted.

The winning stroke was made with one of Thomson's putters.

1958

Natal Open
Feb 6–9
Durban Country Club
Par 74

Gary Player   74–68–71–76: 289
(T. Wilkes   72–72–75–75: 294)

Player's second round broke by two strokes the course record of 70, but he really won the tournament in the third round. Henning and Locke were both starting to challenge, and Locke had played the outward half in 33—the lowest nine holes of the tournament. Player was 1-over at the turn but responded to the pressure by scoring four birdies on the more difficult homeward nine to flatten the hopes of his challengers.

He played the final round very cautiously.

Kentucky Derby Open
April 18–21
Seneca Golf Course, Louisville
Par 72

Gary Player   68–68–69–69: 274
$2,800
(C. Harbert   66–69–74–68: 277)

This was Player's first win in the United States.

In the first round he was out in 32, back in 36, and his 68 put him three behind the leaders. He continued to play careful, accurate golf throughout the tournament, rarely gambling and rarely making a bad shot.

Two strokes behind Paul Harney at the start of the last round, he exchanged birdies with the leader on the early holes but the balance was preserved only until the fifth. Here, Harney dropped two strokes, to dramatically put them level, and then continued to spill strokes, while Player picked up birdies at strategic points.

Australian Open
August 28–30
Kooyonga Golf Club, Adelaide
Par 73

Gary Player   68–67–70–66: 271
(K. Nagle   68–75–67–66: 276)

Player and Nagle shared the lead from the start.

Player started the second round sensationally with an eagle 3 at the long first hole, and when Nagle failed on the greens, Player had a 4-stroke lead. The tournament seemed all over, but Nagle challenged strongly in the third round. At the start of the last round he gained two more strokes on the first three holes; but Player pulled back with two birdies before the turn, both men being out in 33, and went on to a comfortable win.

Nagle's fine last two rounds were no consolation for being three times runner-up in four Opens.

1959

Transvaal Open
Jan 15–17
Kensington Golf Club, Jo'burg
Par 72   6,702 yds

Gary Player   65–70–64–67: 266
£300
(B. Locke   65–69–68–68: 270)

The last round had all the excitement of match play. The old master Locke battled all the way, though vastly out-driven, to hold on with his fabulous short game. But Player was not wanting around the greens either. Responding to what was described as "a great exhibition", the crowd demonstrated an enthusiasm un-equalled in South African golf.

In fact, Player's win could be seen as just reward for his record-equalling 64 in the third round.

South African PGA Matchplay
Feb 5–7
Houghton Golf Club, Jo'burg
Par 72   6,994 yds

Player won the final from Harold Henning by 3 and 1. Player's impres-sive striking of the ball gave him an overall edge, and only in chipping was Henning on terms. Between them, they scored 18 birdies in 35 holes.

In the afternoon, Player went out in five under par and later gained birdies at 14 and 15, in pouring rain, to put him 1-up at a crucial stage.

Natal Open
Feb 27–Mar 3
Durban Country Club
Par 73   6,490 yds

Gary Player   72–67–70–69: 278
£300
(B. Locke   72–71–67–68: 278)

Player won the 36-hole play-off, after a tie had almost seemed a fair end to the tournament. On the last day, 41-year-old Locke gathered all his re-serves together in order to get through the 36 holes of the hilly course: the heat caused him to change out of his favourite plus-fours and to mop his face continually with a towel. In the end Player had to get a birdie at 18 to save the day, and got it by driving the 277-yd green.

After this dramatic tie the play-off threatened to be a let-down. For Locke it was, but not for Player: he struck a dazzling 66, to break Locke's 20-year course record, and then an afternoon 67, to win by seven strokes.

British Open
July 1–3
Muirfield Golf Club,
Scotland
Par 73   6,800 yds

Gary Player   75–71–70–68: 284
£1,000
(F. Van Donck 70–70–73–73: 286)

In the first round, the sand dunes and the many bunkers of Muirfield, plus a freshening wind, gave Player the modest-looking return of 75 for some good golf. He was, however, seven strokes behind the leader, Fred Bullock; after two rounds the margin was eight strokes. After a third round of 70, which made up four strokes on the field, but left nine men still front of him, Player decided that his last round was going to be "66 or bust".

There were several contenders during the last day, but none of them able to dominate it until Player started a charge. The crowd sensed that this was a bid for victory and surged around him. He needed to finish with two 4s for an historic 32 on the inward nine and a magic total of 66. He saved himself at the 17th with a 20-ft putt, and then on the 18th hit a fairway bunker and also three-putted for a miserable six.

He left the course, sure that he had thrown away the championship, only to learn that no one else had been able to take it.

At 23 he was one of the youngest of all Open champions.

Victorian Open
Nov 5–7
Yarra Yarra Golf Club,
Melbourne
Par 73

Gary Player   70–69–69–67: 275
£800
(H. Henning   72–69–65–74: 280)

Henning took the lead in the third round, but Player drew level after five holes of the final round. He was out in 32 and in a killer finish played the last three holes in four under par —including a 40-ft putt for an eagle at 16.

1960

The Masters
Dec 31–Jan 2
Germiston Golf Club
Par 73

Gary Player   74–70–66–71 : 281
£300
(H. Henning   71–67–71–73 : 282)

This "one-off" tournament was partially sponsored by Player and Henning, and in fact they recouped exactly the money they put up. Player's form, however, was lacklustre. Bobby Locke commented: "The ball was not running for him in the final round but his determination was wonderful and I enjoyed watching him. Any other golfer might have been five strokes worse."

Player was disappointed with the total. Nevertheless, his third round 66 was a course record.

Transvaal Open
Jan 7–9
Parkview Golf Club, Jo'burg
Par 72   6,885 yds

Gary Player   66–68–66–71 : 271
£300
(H. Henning   68–66–72–70 : 276)

Player and Henning were level at halfway, Henning having lost a

private wager between them the previous week and evidently being out to make good.

Player seemed unusually irritable in the second round, but swept into the lead in the third. On a course with few 3s or 5s birdies were scarce, but he did not drop a stroke to par in equalling his own course record of 66.

All interest fell away on the last afternoon as Player scored his second successive tournament success.

South African PGA
Jan 21–23
Houghton Golf Club, Jo'burg
Par 72   6,994 yds

Gary Player   67–69–66–64 : 266
£300
(R. Waltman   66–71–74–72 : 283)

Player was only joint leader at the halfway stage, before amassing his 17-stroke winning margin in the final 36 holes.

He three-putted only once in the tournament, and dropped only three strokes to par. At the final green he needed a birdie 3 to break Locke's record for the lowest round in South African golf, and dramatically holed a 25-ft chip.

It was also the first time that anyone had broken 70 in each of four rounds at Houghton, and the club framed the four cards.

Natal Open
Jan 29–31
Royal Durban Golf Club
Par 74

Gary Player   70–67–74–71 : 282
£400
(H. Henning   76–70–70–69 : 285)

On the last day Henning gained ground rapidly and put much pressure on Player, who had led overnight by two strokes. Player missed an inordinate number of short putts (11 from 5 ft and under and three from 18 ins and under).

It was while he was labouring under these setbacks that a roar from the 18th announced that Henning had closed with a birdie for 69. Player responded by birdie-ing three of the next four holes, but he also dropped strokes at two others.

When safely on the green at the 18th he sank a 30-ft birdie putt for victory.

Western Province Open
March 4–6
Royal Cape Golf Club,
Cape Town
Par 72   6,523 yds

Gary Player   71–67–65–68 : 271
£300
(H. Henning   72–65–70–71 : 278)

On a course which was almost reduced to pitch-and-putt in the windless conditions, Denis Hutchinson broke the record in the first round and Harold Henning bettered it in the second. Player was one stroke behind at halfway.

He made short work of catching up as he started a brilliant third round with four birdies and an eagle in the first five holes, and was seven under par at the turn.

South African Open
March 14–16
Mowbray Golf Club,
Cape Town
Par 75

Gary Player   72–72–70–66 : 280
(H. Henning   69–70–74–74 : 287)

An unusual victory, starting with a first round in which Player went out in a delightful 33, then suffered a nightmare of hooking and slicing in a tricky crosswind. He was three off the lead, as Bob Williams equalled the course record of 69.

In the second round he tried to fight the wind, no more successfully, as Henning scored better with relaxed, steady golf. A long eagle putt at the 18th saved Player from greater hardship and kept him in contention, albeit five strokes from Henning.

He was struggling throughout the third round, though he closed the gap to one stroke.

For the final round in the afternoon, he made a change of clothing —to violet trousers and yellow shirt —and struck a dazzling 66, three under the course record, to win by a stunning seven strokes. Again he attacked the course, and this time succeeded. He had a birdie on each of the first three holes, and on each of the last four.

71

1961

San Francisco Open
Jan 26–29
Harding Park Golf Club
Par 71

Gary Player   70–69–68–65: 272
$9,000
(D. Whitt   70–70–66–68: 274)

Player was eight strokes behind at halfway. In the last round he started by holing putts of 24 ft and 37 ft on the first two greens, and got three birdies on the first four holes. Later he made birdies at 15, 16 and 17 with such accurate approach play that he needed putts of only 2, 4 and 5 ft.

All this was achieved in heavy rain and on muddy greens which Casper maintained, in an official complaint, were "unplayable".

Player's great 65 was by three strokes the best round of the last day.

Sunshine Open
March 23–26
Bayshore, Miami Beach
Par 72

Gary Player   69–68–67–69: 273
$3,500
(A. Palmer   68–70–70–66: 274)

This was the "trap shot" win. Player had been tied with Boros and Brewer after three rounds; then Palmer, four

strokes away, made a last round charge.

The pressure went on Player, who was playing immediately behind Palmer, and although he started with a 65-ft putt for an eagle 3 on the first, he later began to drop shots—culminating at 16 and 17, where he three-putted and over-shot the green. He then needed a birdie at the par-5 18th.

His second shot caught a trap 50 yards from the green. Faced with the most difficult of golf shots, he exploded out with "the best trap shot of my life" to within 6 ft, and sank the putt.

US Masters
April 6–11
Augusta National Golf Club
Par 72   6,850 yds

Gary Player   69–68–69–74: 280
$20,000
(A. Palmer   68–69–73–71: 281)

Player came to Augusta as the tour's money leader, and although Palmer was the obvious favourite Player was rated a very strong challenger.

The duel began on the first day, with Palmer sharing the lead on 68 and Player following on 69. A see-saw second round ended with a reverse of the first day's scores, and the two men co-leaders.

When Palmer slipped in the third round, Player led by four strokes. He played perfect golf, in all, for three and a half rounds, but lost his authority at the 13th hole on the last round. Into pine trees, into a ditch, and finally three-putting, he scored a seven which entirely wiped out his lead.

He seemed to have thrown the title away, but Palmer struck bunker trouble on the last hole, lost two strokes, and gave the title back to Player.

Wills Open
Oct 26–28
The Lakes Golf Club, Sydney
Par 72   6,594 yds

Gary Player   78–68–71–69: 286
£800
(E. Cremin   72–71–73–73: 289)

Player was particularly upset by the wind in the first round, though so difficult were the conditions that his 78 still left him sharing fifth place—albeit six strokes off the lead. His second-round course record halved his deficit and on the last day he joined with Nagle in challenging the 47-year-old Cremin.

There was seldom more than one stroke in it, until Player produced the more positive finish over the final nine holes. In the last round he dropped a stroke to par on one hole of the first nine, but on none on the second.

Yomiuri Open
Nov 3–5
Tokyo
Par 72

Gary Player   75–72–72–70: 289
£714
(Chen Ching Po 76–72–71–75: 294)

Player was 10th after the first day. His progression to the front of the tournament was matched by the Nationalist China professional, Chen Ching Po.

On the seventh hole of the final day Player was one stroke behind, at which point he holed his second shot, a 3-wood to the green. This turned the tables, and he went on to disappoint the gallery by beating Chen.

Transvaal Open
Dec 22–24
Germiston Golf Club
Par 73

Gary Player   70–69–67–68: 274
£300
(A. Locke   70–69–72–71: 282)

Dennis Hutchinson led at halfway with two 66s, which put Player seven off the lead when the final day's 36 holes began.

His form was very soon irrepressible, and an eagle at the fifth saw Hutchinson's lead already cut to one stroke. Player eagled the same hole in the afternoon round, as he galloped to an 8-stroke win.

1962

American PGA
July 19–22
Aronimink Golf Club
Par 72

Gary Player   72–67–69–70: 278
$13,000
(B. Goalby   69–72–71–67: 279)

In the year that the "Big Three" became a catch phrase, Palmer had beaten Player in a play-off for the Masters, Nicklaus beat Palmer in a play-off for the US Open, and Palmer won the British Open. Now Player became the first foreigner to win the PGA since 1930.

Nicklaus made a belated run with third and fourth rounds of 69 and 67, but Palmer was always out of contention. Player had been feeling depressed but responded to the lush surroundings. He was six shots off the lead on the first day; his second round 67 put him in a tie for second place; after the third round he led by two strokes.

He was much relieved to hold off Goalby, to win his first US tournament in 15 months and give himself a new lease of life.

Australian Open
Nov 1–3
Royal Adelaide Golf Club
Par 73

Gary Player   69–70–71–71: 281
(K. Nagle   71–68–70–74: 283)

Player led by two strokes after the opening round but was a stroke behind Kel Nagle after the third. On the final day he drew level with a birdie at the first hole, turned three ahead of Nagle—in 34—and held his advantage to the end.

His steadiness in the last round was a reflection of his play throughout the tournament, with each round consistently under par.

Transvaal Open
Dec 13–15
Royal Johannesburg Golf Club
Par 73

Gary Player   74–67–69–69: 279
(R. Charles   75–71–72–69: 287)

Player was one stroke ahead after two rounds, and then walked away with the tournament. Once again his challenger had been Harold Henning, who faded steadily on the last day.

Player also finished 12 strokes clear of Arnold Palmer, to win by six strokes a six-tournament challenge series between him and Palmer.

1963

San Diego Open
Jan 11–14
Stardust Country Club
Par 71 6,800 yds

Gary Player 65–65–70–70: 270
$3,500
(T. Lema 65–68–71–67: 271)

This was his only American win of 1963, though he had a wonderfully consistent string of results which included seven second placings and 13 placings in the top five.

Casper took the lead with a first-round 64 and Player led him by only one stroke as they started the last day paired together. Lema finished ahead of them, though, with a 67 which applied the pressure.

At the final hole, a 207-yd par-3, Player's tee shot finished a foot off the fringe of the green, and he seemed to be heading for a tie. But from 18 ft he sank the putt, much to Lema's disgust, to snatch outright victory.

Australian Open
Oct 31–Nov 2
Royal Melbourne Golf Club
Par 74

Gary Player 70–70–70–68: 278
(B. Devlin 71–72–72–70: 285)

Player started the first round the same day that he stepped off a plane from Paris, via the USA. He got

through the day close to exhaustion, and continued to putt like a genius.

His seven-stroke win was perhaps the most impressive tournament victory of his career.

Open 5000
Nov 21–23
Kensington Golf Club, Jo'burg
Par 72

Gary Player 66–67–70–66: 269
R2,000
(D. Hutchinson 72–68–75–70: 285)

Player increased his lead in every round. Two strokes ahead after the first, six after the second, nine after the third, he extended his lead to 16 with a final 66 shot in pouring rain.

Richelieu Grand Prix
Nov 29–31
King David Country Club, Cape Town
Par 73

Gary Player 70–69–73–71: 283
R1,500
(P. Sewgolum 72–79–74–72: 297)

Player had missed the first leg of this three-tournament series in which the overall winner was to be determined by adding together each man's eight best rounds. Therefore all of Player's, in the remaining two contests, had to count.

On the King David course, where

75

a fresh breeze put scores even higher in the final two rounds, he was the only player to get as low as 70 during the tournament.

Dec 19–21
Kensington Golf Club, Jo'burg
Par 72

Gary Player   68–68–66–69: 271
  R1,500
(D. Hutchinson 70–66–67–69: 272)

This final leg of the Richelieu Grand Prix provided Player with some stern opposition from Dennis Hutchinson. There was never more than two strokes between them, and after his 66 on the final morning Player still led by only one stroke. They were level when, in the final round, Hutchinson birdied at 13, and it needed a 4-ft putt on the last green to win it.

Player headed Hutchinson by four strokes in the overall contest, to win another R2,000.

1964

Dunlop Masters
Jan 2–4
Houghton Golf Club, Jo'burg
Par 72   7,000 yds

Gary Player   70–68–72–75: 285
(B. Locke   69–69–73–76: 287)

A diffident start by Player, who was tired and in need of a break, and he was not lucky with his putting. However, few players found birdies easy on this course, and in a strangely high-scoring third round only four men broke par.

There was controversy in the last round when a storm broke and Player and Locke sheltered after the sixth hole, while others played on.

However, on the resumption, Player lost strokes at 7, 8 and 10, bringing Locke within one stroke. Then he overcame his indifferent form and responded with great birdies at 15 and 16. He could afford to drop a stroke on the last hole.

Pensacola Open
March 5–9
Pensacola Country Club, Florida
Par 72

Gary Player   71–68–66–69: 274
$4,000
(A. Palmer   69–68–68–69: 274)

Player won the 18-hole play-off with a 71 to Palmer's 72 and Barber's 74 (having lost all seven previous play-offs).

There was wind for the first round but Player played well and putted well. In the second round he produced a series of notable sand shots, as he searched hard for his first 1964 win in America. After three rounds he was tied with Palmer and Barber, and they finished likewise.

Player found birdies elusive in the final round: he got one at 14 with a 50-ft putt, but couldn't quite make a 60-footer on the last green for what would have been an outright victory.

Speedway Open
May 28–31
Indianapolis Speedway Golf Course
Par 71

Gary Player   70–66–70–67: 273
$12,000
(D. Sanders   67–71–72–64: 274)

Player was pleased with the driving power—gaining more height and carry—of his fibre-glass shafted clubs.

On the last day, wearing all-white instead of his customary black, he provided a blazing finish to snatch the tournament back from Sanders. He birdied three of the last four holes, including the 18th.

1965

South African Open
Jan 14–16
Royal Cape Golf Club, Cape Town
Par 72   6,752 yds

Gary Player   69–68–67–69 : 273
(D. Hayes   70–68–71–67 : 276)

Young John Inggs had started with a 67, and led for all of the first two days by a solitary stroke—even though in the second round Player had scored five successive birdies in a great homeward run. In the heat of the last day Inggs traded hole for hole.

On the last 18, both men got birdies at 2 and 3, and when Player missed a short putt at 5 they were all square. But Inggs finally cracked on the homeward nine to finish with a 72, while Player went on to victory: to what was to prove the first of five consecutive Opens.

US Open
June 18–21
Bellerive Country Club, St. Louis
Par 70   7,191 yds

Gary Player   70–70–71–71 : 282
$25,000
(K. Nagle   68–73–72–69 : 282)

Player won the 18-hole play-off, 71 to 74. An unexciting Open. On a very long course with huge greens play proceeded rather sedately for three rounds and more.

Nagle, 44 years old, led after the first round; Player moved a stroke ahead of him after two rounds and led by two strokes at the three-quarter stage.

The tournament came to life in the last few holes. At the 16th, a 218-yd par-3 with a colossal green and big bunkers in front, Player bunkered his tee shot and then three-putted. Meanwhile on the 17th Nagle holed a birdie putt, for a swing of three strokes. Both men than played out in pars for the tie.

Player won the play-off rather comfortably and then—the first overseas player in 45 years to win the US Open—donated all of the winning cheque to charity.

World Series
Sept 11–12
Firestone Country Club, Akron, Ohio
Par 70   7,165 yds

Gary Player   70–69 : 139
$50,000
(J. Nicklaus   71–71 : 142)

The others in the field, for golf's richest prize, were Peter Thomson and Dave Marr.

Player, who had rested for three weeks, dropped two strokes on the opening nine holes but with birdies at 12 and 17 gained a lead with his par figures—which elude many pros on this course. In the second round he twice dropped a stroke but also gained three birdies, the most sensational with a 51-ft putt at the 17th, which put paid to Nicklaus's challenge.

No one else scored par or better in the contest and Player himself said he had "never kept the ball in play so well".

World Cup (Individual)
Sept 30–Oct 3
Club de Campo, Madrid
Par 72 6,687 yds

Gary Player   70–69–68–74: 281
(J. Nicklaus   71–72–71–70: 284)

With Henning, Player won the team title for South Africa, and himself led the tournament from start to finish. The two South Africans could afford rounds of 74 and 78 on the last day; they still won the Canada Cup by eight strokes.

Piccadilly World Matchplay
Oct 14–16
Wentworth Golf Club, Surrey
Par 74 6,997 yds

Gary Player defeated:
   N. Coles   5 and 4
   T. Lema   at the 37th
   P. Thomson   3 and 2   £5,000

The famous match came in the semifinal against the late Tony Lema, and was perhaps the most thrilling match of all time.

In the morning Player lost seven holes in a row as Lema hit six birdies

—and scored the second nine in 32. Just after the start of the afternoon 18 Player was 7-down with 17 to play; even after getting three birdies he was still 5-down with nine to play. He then won the 10th, 11th, 13th and 16th, and at the 18th hit one of the best shots of his life—a 3-wood with a controlled draw, which finished 10 ft from the hole and allowed a birdie.

The squared match was won at the first of the sudden-death holes, with another birdie.

Australian Open
Oct 28–31
Kooyonga Golf Club, Adelaide
Par 73 6,736 yds

Gary Player   62–71–62–69: 264
(J. Nicklaus   66–63–70–71: 270)

Player's first round lowered the course record by four strokes, and the Australian Open record by three.

His outward half, 28, established a world record. He started with an eagle 3, followed by five birdies—all this with the temperature in the 90s. He was disappointed that a 5 and 4 at the end foiled his ambition to break 60.

Although he led by four strokes this position was stunningly reversed by Nicklaus's second-round 63, and Player needed a further 62 to cause his opposition to submit.

He might have broken the world record for a national title (263) but took a 5 in trying for a short cut on the 18th, a dog-leg par-4.

79

1966

Transvaal Open
Jan 27–29
Parkview Golf Club, Jo'burg
Par 72

Gary Player   65–69–68–69: 271
R700
(H. Henning   70–70–66–72: 278)

A return to form by Player, and he dominated from start to finish. The 17-under-par total was the lowest of the season and his first-round 65 was a course record.

Natal Open
Feb 4–6
Royal Durban Golf Club
Par 72   6,554 yds

Gary Player   68–74–72–72: 286
R700
(C. Legrange   70–70–72–76: 288)

Player's first round was sensational as, in pelting rain, he reached the turn in a three-over-par 38, debated the weather with officials, and then made nonsense of the conditions by producing a string of five successive birdies from the 10th.

In his nine-hole score of 30 he holed, on sodden greens, twice from 20 ft and on the 18th from 45 ft for an eagle.

South African Open
Feb 17–19
Houghton Golf Club, Jo'burg
Par 72   7,115 yds

Gary Player   70–68–70–70: 278
R900
(H. Henning   69–69–70–71: 279)

A very evenly contested championship came to a climax when, in the third round, Henning had an outward half of 32 and led Player by two strokes.

The last round was a thrilling race to the end, with both players adding to the tension by dropping strokes and picking up birdies. A chip at the 16th from long grass behind the green, to within inches of the hole, virtually gave Player the title.

Piccadilly World Matchplay
Oct 6–8
Wentworth Golf Club, Surrey
Par 74   6,997 yds

Gary Player defeated:
   N. Coles   1 up
   A. Palmer   2 and 1
   J. Nicklaus   6 and 4   £5,000

At the end of a comparatively low year for Player, this was a revitalizing tournament. The competition produced a very high standard of play from Player, Nicklaus, Palmer and Casper; furthermore, Player had to first survive a stiff challenge from Neil Coles, an outstanding match player.

Coles was 1-up after 18 holes, with a 68 to Player's 69, and Player won a tense contest only at the 36th, as he scored 69 to Coles's 70. In the semi-final with Palmer, both men scored 68s to be level after 18 holes, before Player's deadly short game gained him the advantage.

In the final Player was at his very best, and it was too much even for Nicklaus, who found the pressure getting him into trouble. Player scored 67 for the first 18, to go 4-up, and although Nicklaus matched him with 33 for the first nine holes of the afternoon, he could not dent Player's lead.

Indeed Player extended it to win 6 and 4, and Nicklaus was left to reflect: "I don't think anybody living could have played better golf than he did today."

1966 Summary

World Stroke Average
Player (19th)   71.436

World Money List
Player (29th) $48,331

1967

South African Open
Feb 9–11
East London Golf Club, Jo'burg
Par 72   6,631 yds

Gary Player   71–68–71–69: 279
R1,500
(A. Henning   71–67–74–70: 282)

Player was reckoned the man least likely to make a mistake on a course which, although short, was narrow and bush-lined. He was hard pressed in the early rounds and trailed by four strokes after the first round and by one after the second, but he came through like a champion.

This was his third Open in a row, and his total easily beat Bobby Locke's course record of 288 set in 1937.

Dunlop Masters
Feb 16–20
Houghton Golf Club, Jo'burg
Par 72   7,115 yds

Gary Player   68–69–70–72: 279
R700
(C. Legrange   68–74–67–72: 281)

Practically a "home" course, and one of the longest in the country. Alan Henning took the lead with 66 and led at halfway by one stroke from Player, who was frustrated by the greens. Henning crashed with a 76 in the third round, and Player's 70 was enough to maintain control.

His moderate play made the last round anticlimactic.

1967 Summary
World Stroke Average
Player (3rd)   70.48
World Money List
Player (21st) $69,055

1968

South African Open

Jan 18–22
Houghton Golf Club,
Jo'burg
Par 72   7,115 yds

Gary Player   70–65–70–69: 274
R1,500
(C. Legrange   70–67–71–73: 281)

Player's fourth successive Open win. He played well in the first round without getting the score to show for it, but started the second round with three birdies in a row, and later added a 50-ft putt.

He was annoyed with 3-putts in his third-round 70, but Legrange made the mistakes early in the last round to let Player coast home.

Natal Open

Feb 9–11
Royal Durban Golf Club
Par 72   6,554 yds

Gary Player   72–69–72–68: 281
R700
(C. Legrange   71–68–75–73: 287)

On the last day it was Legrange, chasing an elusive first win over Player, who threatened a head-to-head challenge over 36 holes. But the battle was not protracted, as Legrange's putting, especially, was affected by the hard greens.

Player settled in after lunch by starting the final round with successful putts of 30, 40 and 50 ft, as he made four birdies in the first six holes.

Western Province Open

Feb 15–17
King David Golf Club,
Cape Town
Par 73   6,900 yds

Gary Player   75–69–66–70: 280
R700
(C. Clark   73–71–67–73: 284)

A very tentative first round left Player seven strokes off the lead. His second-round 69 was the day's best round and brought him within two strokes, and in the third round he broke up the tournament with a course-record 66.

Clive Clark threatened some opposition with a 67, but in the final round Player sewed it up by going five strokes ahead after six holes.

British Open

July 10–13
Carnoustie Golf Club,
Scotland
Par 72   7,252 yds

Gary Player   74–71–71–73: 289
£3,000
(R. Charles   72–72–71–76: 291)

Player came to Carnoustie with the top stroke-average on the American circuit but without having won a tournament there. The course was a formidable opponent, and all week it seemed that it won. On the first day only four players broke par, as the afternoon breeze freshened from a balmy morning. Player was disgusted with his 74, but still he was only four strokes off the lead.

Casper took the lead in the second round with a great 68. Player regained confidence with a 71, having realized that high scores were to be expected.

A 74 by Casper in the third round brought Player and Charles within two strokes.

In the last round—in which only one player on the day broke par— Player led at the fifth, was later caught by Casper and Charles, but never overtaken. Gutsy golf, and a remarkable championship shot, was his 3-wood on the 14th, of which he said later: "I had to lean sideways to see the pin." It finished two feet from the hole.

Player claimed it was the best he had ever played, on the hardest course he had ever played.

World Series
Sept 7–8
Firestone Country Club, Akron
Par 70   7,180 yds

Gary Player   71–72: 143
  $50,000
(B. Goalby   72–71: 143)

Player won the sudden-death play-off with a birdie at the fourth hole. The tournament started with Player scoring bogeys on two of the first four holes, while Masters' winner Goalby suffered five bogeys on the front nine. Both recovered, and Player led at the end of the first day.

The lead alternated on the second and final day, and by the 18th Boros had joined Player and Goalby in a three-way tie. Player had to save himself from rough and from behind trees, and did it by hitting a 4-iron to within 20 ft. Goalby was short with a 6-iron to the green, but joined the tie. Boros yanked his 3-ft putt and thus missed the play-off.

World Matchplay
Oct 10–13
Wentworth Golf Club, Surrey
Par 74   6,997 yds

Gary Player defeated:
  P. Thomson   8 and 7
  T. Jacklin   at the 37th
  R. Charles   1 up   £5,000

In the process of sweeping aside Thomson in the first match, Player went around the 18 holes of a muddy course in 66 to Thomson's 76.

A good recovery by Jacklin highlighted the semi-final; in terrible weather and on sodden greens which were barely playable, Jacklin scored six birdies to Player's three on the last nine holes, and Player's victory was finally won amidst tension, a partisan crowd and controversy.

The final, against the dispassionate Charles, was no anticlimax. There was never more than one hole between the two golfers, except when Player won the 27th only to be immediately hauled back by Charles's winning of the next two holes.

The fact that Charles's putting was not quite up to his own exceptional standard may have represented the margin between them on the day; nevertheless, Player demonstrated once again that he was a king of match play.

Wills Masters
Nov 7–10
Manly Golf Club, Sydney
Par 73   6,949 yds

Gary Player   69–70–66–72: 277
   A $2,000
(P. Townsend   69–65–74–69: 277)

Player won the sudden-death play-off. He had taken the lead in the third round of the tournament, to lead at this stage by two strokes.

He dropped some strokes to par in the last round, and a birdie putt by Townsend on the 18th made the finish a cliffhanger. Player played the 18th safely for a par, and won the play-off when Townsend missed par on the third hole.

1968 Summary
World Stroke Average
Player (3rd)   70.19
World Money List
Player (8th) $130,012

1969

South African Open
Feb 12–15
Durban Country Club
Par 72   6,570 yds

Gary Player   67–70–72–64: 273
R2,000
(T. Wilkes   69–68–73–69: 279)

To tie Locke's record of five successive Open wins, Player had to survive terrific public pressure. He also needed a hot and cold shower routine to ease a stiff neck immediately before the last round. He then demoralised the field by starting with birdie, par, eagle, birdie.

His last-round 64 was a course record, and he also tied the Open total record.

South African PGA
Feb 19–22
Germiston Golf Club
Par 71   6,980 yds

Gary Player   67–68–66–71: 272
R1,100
(C. Legrange   71–68–67–67: 273)

Player shared the lead from the first round, but had a royal battle with Bobby Cole on the last afternoon—lost by Cole on the last hole, a 205-yd par-3.

Tournament of Champions
April 17–20
La Costa Country Club, California
Par 72   7,114 yds

Gary Player   69–74–69–72: 284
$30,000
(L. Trevino   74–68–70–74: 286)

On this long course with heavy rough and narrow fairways only Player and Trevino finished under par for the tournament. But Player was one of several who, nonetheless, liked the fact that this was a test of golf rather than simply of long hitting.

Australian Open
Oct 23–26
Royal Sydney Golf Club
Par 72   6,722 yds

Gary Player   74–69–68–77: 288
A$2,500
(G. Wolsten-
  holme   71–71–71–76: 289)

Extremely tough—some said sadistic —pin placements on the first day meant high scores, and Player was only three strokes off the lead with his 74.

He played well in the first round but scored better in the second and third. Having been in trouble with his putting, on very tricky greens, he worked hard on this between rounds.

He effectively won the tournament with his third-round 68.

He survived a violent storm on the last afternoon, and great tension on the last green before making a vital par-4.

1969 Summary

World Stroke Average
Player (2nd)   70.49

World Money List
Player (7th) $140,384

1970

Greater Greensboro Open
April 2–5
Sedgefield Country Club, Greensboro
Par 71 7,034 yds

Gary Player 70–63–73–65: 271
$36,000
(M. Baker 69–64–72–68: 273)

It was a significant achievement for Player to win in the fourth week of his return to the US circuit, and despite the pressure of threats to his life and the need to be guarded.

For all his second-round 63 (which tied him in third place) he really won on the last day. The turning point was his holing of a bunker shot for an eagle.

Australian Open
Oct 22–25
Kingston Heath Golf Club, Victoria
Par 72 6,797 yds

Gary Player 71–65–70–74: 280
A$2,850
(B. Devlin 74–72–68–69: 283)

A record sixth win by Player. He thought he had no chance after a nagging hook caused him to miss eight greens in the first round, when only his putting saved him.

He straightened his problems out admirably, to score a course-record 65 on the second day, and on the final day was never really threatened.

Dunlop International
Oct 29–Nov 1
Royal Canberra Golf Club
Par 72

Gary Player 71–67–73–71: 282
A$3,800
(W. Brask 69–73–71–70: 283)

Player was not happy with his game in this, the showpiece of the Australian circuit. He had the lead at no point until the last afternoon. With several players in keen contention, one after another squandered their chances, and Player's temperament won the day—on his 35th birthday.

1970 Summary
World Stroke Average
Player (15th) 71.03
World Money List
Player (16th) $119,645

At home with Player and family

Vivienne's father is still Gary's main coach. Here they're working on taking the club back "in one piece". As if on a refresher course, they discuss all the small details of basic golf: stance, alignment, position of the club at the top. They experiment and explore, they discuss the technique of other golfers. They leave no stone unturned. And they leave no golf ball un-hit. Player drives away, despatching great piles of balls, until about two hours have passed and it is dark.

The house is splendid, but the most precious foods are the simplest. In the saucepan the "mealie meal", the unsifted maize, is being boiled up like porridge. The celery is there to be plucked out and chewed at any time along with carrots. Also present are jars of vitamin C and E, bran and orange juice.

Elder daughter Michelle does the splits; younger daughter Theresa is as versatile standing. Both have represented their province at gymnastics.

Michelle and Theresa, hand-standing with their father, once went happily through the same somersaults that Amanda Leigh now enjoys.

Time for Amanda Leigh to go to bed, and another welcome opportunity for a hug and kiss. Love and emotion is easily expressed in the Player household: affection and laughter are as important as sports and fitness. Vivienne Player was a two-handicap golfer and swam for the province; the two elder daughters are also representative swimmers, as well as gymnasts; and son Wayne is following his father as a professional golfer.

On his 4,000 acre ranch at Colesburg is where Player says he is most at home. "Putting up fences, driving tractors, baling hay, riding horses, training horses, laying bricks, digging trenches, cleaning out the stables . . ." Dogs and horses seem to play important roles in this happy existence. At left, a training track for the Player thoroughbreds, and discussion with farm manager Doug Davies. Right, Kruger the alsatian is being calmed down before the journey back to Johannesburg, which the entire family always makes by train. Willy Betha, a highly valued employee for 40 years, holds the leash. "I love the farm," says Player. "It's my greatest happiness. There's never a day goes by, when I'm on the golf circuit, that I don't think about the farm and yearn for it."

1971

Dunlop Masters
Jan 13–16
Kensington Golf Club, Jo'burg
Par 70   6,774 yds

Gary Player   64–68–69–68 : 269
R2,000
(H. Henning   66–66–67–72 : 271)

The two best players in the tournament decided it utterly between them. In the rarefied atmosphere of 6,000 ft, where a ball will travel far, Player's first-round 64 broke the course record and represented some of the best golf he had ever played in South Africa.

He lost the lead in the third round but in the end took the drama out of the expected last-round showdown by birdie-ing three holes in succession and later getting an eagle.

General Motors Open
Jan 26–29
Wedgewood Country Club, Port Elizabeth
Par 71   6,457 yds

Gary Player   66–69–70–71 : 276
R1,800
(P. Oosterhuis 70–74–72–69 : 285)

His 66 on a blustery opening day gave Player a two-stroke lead, and this was never threatened, nor even reduced, throughout the tournament.

Western Province Open
Feb 6–9
Rondebosch Golf Club
Par 71   6,770 yds

Gary Player   67–68–67–66 : 268
R2,000
(H. Henning   71–67–70–67 : 275)

But for a course record of 66 in the first round by Craig Shankland, Player would have again led from start to finish. However, this was his third victory in three tournaments, and represented one of the "hottest streaks" of his career.

Greater Jacksonville Open
March 18–21
Hidden Hills Country Club
Par 72   6,943 yds

Gary Player   70–70–72–69 : 281
$25,000
(H. Underwood   69–70–71–71 : 281)

Player won the sudden-death play-off at the second hole—reversing the pattern of nine losses in ten previous play-off experiences.

The victory came in the fourth tournament of his return to the US circuit, having finished fourth in his first, the PGA.

National Airlines Open
March 25–28
Miami Country Club
Par 72   6,970 yds

Gary Player   69–67–70–68: 274
$40,000
(L. Trevino   67–69–71–69: 276)

A solid 67 in difficult conditions in the second round set up this win. In the last round Player disengaged himself from a substantial number of contenders by twice scoring a succession of three birdies.

It was the first time he had won consecutive tournaments in the United States.

Player won for the fourth time in eight years, having played in all eight, and in the process sorted out worrying problems with the hook.

In the final he hooked the ball six times in the morning, but putted "as well as I possibly can". Nicklaus led by one hole after the morning 18 (with a 67 to Player's 68). Player practised in the lunch break and, having struggled to stay with Nicklaus in the morning, dramatically turned the scales on the resumption.

Putting like a genius and scoring birdies while Nicklaus dropped one stroke, Player took the first four holes of the afternoon 18, which set him fair for a comfortable victory.

Piccadilly World Matchplay
Oct 7–9
Wentworth Golf Club,
Surrey
Par 74   6,997 yds

Gary Player defeated:
T. Jacklin   4 and 3
R. Charles   2 and 1
J. Nicklaus   5 and 4   £8,500

1971 Summary
World Stroke Average
Player (3rd)   70.3
World Money List
Player (4th) $167,035

1972

Western Province Open
Jan 12–14
Royal Cape Golf Club
Par 72   6,871 yds

Gary Player   69–69–67–73: 278
R2,000
(C. Legrange   69–70–69–74: 282)

Player's first tournament in two months, but he raced off to an impressive start, an early eagle making him four under par after seven holes.

He experienced difficulty with the putting surfaces but was never seriously challenged, and his anticlimactic last round of 73 actually added a stroke to his lead.

Dunlop Masters (I)
Jan 19–22
Kensington Golf Club, Jo'burg
Par 71   6,799 yds

Gary Player   71–65–65–66: 267
R1,800
(B. Cole   67–68–66–69: 270)

Player was seven strokes adrift after his opening round of 71, which on this low-scoring course was bettered by half the field.

After two rounds, Player was still six strokes behind the precocious leader, 18-year-old amateur Robby Meier, but level after three rounds. They played the last round together,

Player scoring 66 (with an outward half of 30) and Meier 74.

South African Open
Feb 9–12
Royal Johannesburg Golf Club
Par 73   7,176 yds

Gary Player   69–71–66–68: 274
R2,500
(B. Cole   67–70–69–69: 275)

Player trailed Harold Henning by five strokes at the halfway stage and was despondent at his form. With the course playing very easily and the greens perfect, Player's third round 66 was in fact marked by bad shots and brilliant recoveries.

He broke free from the field with a run of four birdies at 6, 7, 8 and 9, to win the Open for the eighth time and with a record aggregate.

New Orleans Open
March 23–26
Lakewood Country Club
Par 72   7,080 yds

Gary Player   73–69–68–69: 279
$25,000
(J. Nicklaus   66–70–71–73: 280)

A remarkable win, after being seven strokes behind with a loose 73 in the first round.

Even after three rounds he was three strokes behind Nicklaus and Casper. But after 11 holes of the final round he had taken the lead, and made par for each subsequent hole.

Japan Airlines Open
May 11–14
Narashino Country Club, Chiba
Par 72   7,071 yds

Gary Player   67–71–72–70: 280
$6,494
(H. Yasuda   68–73–72–68: 281)

Player salvaged his one-stroke win with a masterly splash from a deep and wet bunker at the 18th, the ball finishing 3 ft from the pin.

He said it was the most difficult par he had ever had to make to win a tournament.

American PGA
August 3–6
Oakland Hills, Birmingham, Michigan
Par 70   7,054 yds

Gary Player   71–77–67–72: 281
$45,000
(J. Jamieson   69–72–72–70: 283)

Some thought the course too difficult, but Player called it "the toughest and best course in America". He took a one-stroke lead in the third round.

On the final day, in depressing drizzle, he dropped a stroke on three of the first four holes, and made more mistakes towards the finish—but virtually won the tournament with an improbable short-cut shot, with a 9-iron which had to travel 150 yds, high over trees and also clear water.

World Series
Sept 9–10
Firestone Country Club, Akron
Par 70   7,180 yds

Gary Player   71–71: 142
$50,000
(J. Nicklaus   75–69: 144)

This was Player's third win in the tournament contested exclusively by major title winners.

Comparatively high scoring was the result of a gusty wind and the rough condition of the course, on which Player manoeuvred the ball with typical dexterity.

Brazilian Open
Nov 16–19
La Gavea Golf Club, Rio de Janeiro
Par 69

Gary Player   65–68–68–69: 270
(S. Melnyk   69–71–69–71: 280)

Player dominated a tournament in which, on a hilly seaside course, and amidst heat and humidity, scoring was not low. He was disappointed with his second round and practised for three hours afterwards, yet still returned the same score in the third.

His last round par was his highest score of the four rounds.

Dunlop Masters (II)
Nov 29–Dec 2
Kensington Golf Club, Jo'burg
Par 70   6,774 yds

Gary Player   65–68–68–67: 268
R2,500
(H. Henning   70–66–67–66: 269)

After rain had interrupted the first day's play, Player resumed by making a spectacular three birdies on the last five holes. But when the final day began Irishman John O'Leary had a three-stroke lead.

Pressure from the South Africans, Player and Henning, gnawed away at O'Leary, who finished (when he seemed to be headed for a play-off with Player) by hitting his second shot on the last hole into the water.

1972 Summary
World Stroke Average
Player (3rd)   70.9
World Money List
Player (3rd) $219,599

93

1973

Southern Open
Sept 6–9
Green Island Country Club, Columbus
Par 70   6,791 yds

Gary Player   69–65–67–69: 270
$20,030
(F. Fezler   69–68–66–68: 271)

Player's first big win after an operation and his first win in the US for a year, was achieved while his major rivals were contesting the World Series.

He was not pressed quite as hard as the scores might suggest. Having been always close to the lead—in fact never more than two strokes away—he played his best golf in the last round.

With two strokes to play he had established a five-stroke lead before Fezler made two birdies while Player dropped two strokes to par.

Piccadilly World Matchplay
Oct 11–13
Wentworth Golf Club, Surrey
Par 74   6,997 yds

Gary Player defeated:
T. Jacklin 3 and 2
J. Miller 3 and 2
G. Marsh at 40th hole £10,000

What had looked like an undramatic final suddenly caught fire after Player had gone 2-up with four to play.

With two birdies for Marsh, and Player three-putting, Marsh won three holes in a row and went to the 36th 1-up. Player, who had never lost a Piccadilly final, saved his bacon with a 6-ft putt which dramatically dropped into the cup after it had seemed to have stopped.

In the sudden-death extra holes he twice more saved himself with bunker recoveries, and at the 40th sank an 8-ft putt while Marsh missed from 4 ft.

1973 Summary
World Stroke Average
Player (=13th)   71.1
World Money List
Player (21st) $104,765

1974

Dunlop Masters
Jan 23–26
Kensington Golf Club, Jo'burg
Par 70   6,774 yds

Gary Player   69–66–70–65 : 270
R2,500
(B. Cole   69–64–67–70 : 270)

Player won the sudden-death play-off at the second hole, and called it "my most exciting win in South Africa".

Cole had been in outstanding form throughout a week of very low scoring, and looked like an easy winner after three rounds. In the final round he was six strokes ahead after six holes.

Thereafter, he twice lost two strokes on one hole, while Player with much improved putting and his customary top-class bunker play finally closed the gap on the 18th.

General Motors International
Feb 6–9
Wedgewood Park, Port Elizabeth
Par 74   7,100 yds

Gary Player   71–70–71–71 : 283
R3,100
(J. Fourie   76–71–71–70 : 288)

After three rounds Player led by two strokes and looked like an easy winner, but when he let strokes slip Baiocchi and Fourie became challengers.

At the 12th, Baiocchi was leading by one stroke. A galvanised Player began a charge which took him through the last six holes in four under par.

The climax came at 17, when Baiocchi chipped in for a birdie and Player chipped in for an eagle.

US Masters
April 11–14
Augusta National Golf Club
Par 72   7,020 yds

Gary Player   71–71–66–70 : 278
$35,000
(T. Weiskopf   71–69–70–70 : 280)

The famous course was like a "sleeping giant" in the words of one competitor, and Player was in 16th place after each of his 71s.

He became a contender between the 12th and 16th holes of the third round, when he scored five consecutive birdies.

Under pressure in the final round, he finally settled the contest with a memorable 9-iron to the 17th hole that settled literally inches from the pin.

Memphis Classic
May 23–26
Colonial Country Club
Par 72   7,173 yds

Gary Player   65–72–69–67: 273
$35,000
(L. Graham   67–71–67–70: 275)

Player took the course record in the first round; but when the final round started he was four strokes behind the leader Hubert Green.

The turning point came at the par-3 12th where Green put his tee shot 10 ft from the hole and Player went over into a bunker: from 40 ft away, Player blasted into the cup, then Green missed his putt. Player had two strokes and kept them.

British Open
July 10–13
Royal Lytham & St. Anne's
Par 71   6,822 yds

Gary Player   69–68–75–70: 282
£5,500
(P. Oosterhuis 71–71–73–71: 286)

In all the tournament there were only seven rounds under 70, four of them by players on the last day who were out of contention and had nothing to lose. So Player's first two rounds, especially, were a triumph for iron play on the narrow sun-baked fairways, with the wind blowing hard.

He was tied after the first round with the little known British professional John Morgan, and after a birdie on the first hole of the second round he was out in front all the way. His second round 68 when the wind was at its strongest, was the lowest of the championship, and considered one of the great championship rounds.

After it, he led by five strokes and had established a position from which he dominated the championship.

Australian Open
Oct 31–Nov 3
Lake Karrinyup Golf Club, Perth
Par 72   6,520 yds

Gary Player   69–72–63–73: 277
(N. Wood   73–67–69–71: 280)

A record-shattering 63 on the Saturday comprised nine birdies and nine pars, and was achieved in blustery conditions. As a result Player took a five-stroke lead into the final round. He slumped midway through the round and started the final nine only one stroke ahead, then he took a two-over-par 6 at the 11th.

The position was soon reversed in Player's favour when at 14 he sank a birdie putt while Wood 3-putted.

Ibergolf European Champions
Nov 9–10
Las Lomas, Madrid
Par 72

Gary Player   73–72: 145
£3,000
(P. Townsend   73–72: 145)

Having tied this 36-hole tournament, Player won the play-off at the 2nd hole.
Earlier, Townsend had led but slipped from the 15th onwards. Player caught him dramatically on the 18th when, with his ball blocked by a bush, and the shot needing to carry 200 yds of lake if he was to make the green, he put it 20 ft from the hole—thus ensuring a tie and a play-off.

General Motors International
Nov 20–23
Wedgewood Park, Port Elizabeth
Par 74   7,100 yds

Gary Player   71–67–72–70: 280
R3,100
(A. Ooster-
huizen   70–66–74–71: 281)

A two-man race from the second round onwards, where both played flawlessly. All scores went up with the wind on the third day, and Player and Oosterhuizen shared the lead on 210.
The last day saw a battle royal, with Oosterhuizen adding to the drama by constantly saving himself after getting into trouble. At the 17th they were level, and even though a wild drive by Oosterhuizen cost him par, to Player's birdie, he then birdied 18 to force Player to sink another birdie from 12 ft.

Brazil Open
Nov 28–Dec 1
La Gavea, Rio de Janeiro
Par 69

Gary Player   67–59–70–71: 267
(M. Hayes   69–65–66–72: 272)

Player destroyed the field—and the tournament—with his second-round 59 which equalled the world record (Snead's) for a tournament round, and which put him nine strokes clear at the halfway stage.

1974 Summary
World Stroke Average
Player (2nd)   69.8
World Money List
Player (5th) $218,388

1975

South African Open
Jan 29–Feb 1
Mowbray Golf Club,
Cape Town
Par 72   6,850 yds

Gary Player   68–67–72–71: 278
R3,100
(A. Henning   73–70–70–71: 284)

There was little doubt Player would win from the moment he shot 68 in the violently windy weather (with gusts up to 50 mph) of the first day. He scored 14 pars and two birdies in his 68, and his control of the ball was regarded as remarkable. Player himself rated this round better than his famous 59 in the Brazilian Open.

He was six strokes clear at the start and the end of the South African Open's last day, and his ninth win matched Bobby Locke's record of Open wins.

Lancome Trophy
Oct 9–12
Saint-Nom-la-Bretche,
Paris
Par 72   7,038 yds

Gary Player   73–65–69–71: 278
$17,000
(L. Wadkins   72–70–72–72: 286)

Player started by suffering his nemesis, the hook, and ended the first day over halfway down the field. He worked on the problem overnight.

However, the next day it was his celebrated sand wedge play (with a brand-new wedge) which aided him to a course record.

At this stage Jacklin led by one stroke, but when Jacklin's game came apart in the third round, Player's 69 gave him a six-stroke lead—which he preserved throughout a calm final round.

General Motors International
Dec 10–13
Wedgewood Park,
Port Elizabeth
Par 74   7,100 yds

Gary Player   74–70–68–73: 285
R3,100
(J. Fourie   67–70–75–76: 288)

Once again, John Fourie had a substantial lead and lost.

After the first round he led the field by three strokes and Player by seven; after the second he led the field by six strokes and Player by seven.

The lead vanished in the third round, which left Fourie and Player level on 212, with no one else in contention; and when Fourie resumed badly the next day it was all over.

1975 Summary
World Stroke Average
Player (9th)   71.2
World Money List
Player (17th) $114,958

1976

Dunlop Masters (I)
Feb 4–7
Kensington Golf Club, Jo'burg
Par 70   6,774 yds

Gary Player   68–63–67–70: 268
R2,750
(C. Legrange   69–66–69–65: 269)

It was a two-man race at the end, but for a long time there had been no contest.

There was a lot of rain during the tournament and several postponements, one of which stopped Player when, in the second round, he had played nine holes in 30 and was looking to break 60.

His score after three rounds was 198, one of the best ever in South Africa. He was five strokes clear of Henning, and six of Legrange; but a cautious last round, with 15 consecutive pars, gave Legrange the incentive to score birdies and catch him.

Legrange, however, dropped a stroke at 16, and Player sank a 20-ft putt for his first, crucial, birdie.

Dunlop Masters (II)
Nov 3–6
Kensington Golf Club, Jo'burg
Par 70   6,774 yds

Gary Player   67–65–70–68: 270
R4,000
(H. Baiocchi   70–69–69–66: 274)

Having not won a tournament since the start of the year, Player won this one emphatically. He was two strokes clear at halfway, and although he slipped in the third round none of those in contention was able to make up ground.

It was his 10th Dunlop win; he had won all but one of the previous seven.

South African Open
Nov 24–27
Durban Country Club
Par 72   6,558 yds

Gary Player   70–68–73–69: 280
R6,000
(B. Verwey   72–72–70–72: 286)

This was not the runaway win the scores might suggest.

Player led after every round, including the first which was affected by an antagonistic wind in the afternoon, but a five-stroke lead at halfway was reduced to only one stroke at three-quarter distance.

He pulled away steadily in the last round for his tenth South African Open, which beat Bobby Locke's record.

1976 Summary
World Stroke Average
Player (3rd)   70.7
World Money List
Player (27th) $119,718

1977

South African Open
Nov 9–12
Royal Johannesburg
Golf Club
Par 72

Gary Player   69–71–63–70: 273
R6,700
(D. Hayes   73–68–65–70: 276)

Player's third-round 63 was a record, and with his fourth round 70 he completed 38 consecutive holes without losing a stroke to par—a distinction he could perhaps attribute to a return to his old blade putter.

Having virtually won the tournament in the third round, the last day appeared a cruise; the only cloud in the sky was the intrusion, again, of putting problems; but this could not seriously impede him in going to his 11th Open title.

ICL International
Nov 16–19
Kensington Golf Club,
Jo'burg
Par 70   6,774 yds

Gary Player   67–66–66–69: 268
R4,000
(B. Cole   70–64–63–73: 270)

The course took a fearful beating, with 62 the lowest round. Despite his low scoring, Player was trailing by two strokes after three rounds and when he double-bogeyed the opening hole of the final round he was four strokes behind.

Cole also played raggedly and the tournament seemed to be lost by him rather than won by Player.

World Cup (Individual)
Dec 8–11
Wack Wack Golf Club,
Manila
Par 72   7,134 yds

Gary Player   72–68–73–76: 289
(R. Lovares   73–69–77–73: 292)

In all the tournament there were only four rounds below 70, of which Player's second-round 68 was the best. Hubert Green and local star Rudy Lavares were close after two rounds, then both took 77s in the third.

1977 Summary
World Stroke Average
Player (4th)   71.05
World Money List
Player (14th) $145,413

1978

US Masters
April 6–9
Augusta National Golf Club
Par 72

Gary Player   72–72–69–64: 277
$45,000
(T. Watson   73–68–68–69: 278)

Player had barely hinted at being a challenger in the early rounds, and was lying 10th when the last day started, eight strokes from the lead.

Even after eight holes he had gained only one stroke on the overnight leader, Hubert Green. He then birdied seven of the next 10 and finished by holing from 20 ft above the hole on the last green. During the last round he passed 16 men.

His third Masters title, at the age of 42, was one of golf's famous victories. His last round was in fact the lowest final round by a Masters' winner.

Tournament of Champions
April 13–16
La Costa Golf Club,
San Diego
Par 72   6,889 yds

Gary Player   70–68–76–67: 281
$45,000
(A North   76–70–68–69: 283)

Player felt ill on the third day, evidently through food poisoning, and started the last day seven strokes off the lead.

The final round turned out to be almost a replica of the Masters. With the wind gusting, Player birdied four of the first seven holes and was tied for the lead after only nine holes. In the end he could afford to drop a stroke to par on the 18th and still win by two strokes.

In the course of the last round he overtook leader Ballesteros, who struggled in with a 79, and pulled rapidly away from Nicklaus, who took 77.

Houston Open
April 20–23
Woodlands Golf Club
Par 72

Gary Player   64–67–70–69: 270
(A. Bean   67–65–66–73: 271)

Player's succession of victories—three in a row—was the best since Hubert Green in 1976, and the best on the American circuit by a foreigner since Bobby Locke in 1947. After his opening 64, which gave him a one-stroke lead, Player started the last day three strokes behind Andy Bean.

101

The last round pressure, however, seemed to suit Player better than Bean, and after Bean had lost strokes around the turn, birdies by Player at 16 and 17 brought him home.

1978 Summary

World Stroke Average
Player (13th)   71.22
World Money List
Player (11th) $205,157